Man and Aggression

Edited by
M. F. ASHLEY MONTAGU

OXFORD UNIVERSITY PRESS
London   Oxford   New York
1968

OXFORD UNIVERSITY PRESS

Oxford   London   New York
Glasgow   Toronto   Melbourne   Wellington
Cape Town   Salisbury   Ibadan   Nairobi   Lusaka   Addis Ababa
Bombay   Calcutta   Madras   Karachi   Lahore   Dacca
Kuala Lumpur   Hong Kong   Tokyo

Copyright © 1968 by M. F. Ashley Montagu
Library of Congress Catalogue Card Number: 68-29723
First published by Oxford University Press, New York, 1968
First published as an Oxford University Press paperback, 1968
Printed in the United States of America

To Morris Ginsberg

Contributors

S. A. Barnett, *University of Glasgow*

John Beatty, *Brooklyn College*

Kenneth E. Boulding, *University of Colorado*

Sally Carrighar, *Guernsey, Channel Islands*

John Hurrell Crook, *University of Bristol*

Geoffrey Gorer, *Haywards Heath, Sussex*

Ralph Holloway, *Columbia University*

Edmund Leach, *King's College, Cambridge*

M. F. Ashley Montagu, *Columbia University*

Marshall D. Sahlins, *University of Michigan*

T. C. Schneirla, *The American Museum of Natural History*

J. P. Scott, *Bowling Green State University, Ohio*

Omer C. Stewart, *University of Colorado*

Sir Solly Zuckerman, *Zoological Society, London*

Contents

Introduction

The purpose of this book is to inquire into the validity of the views
on human nature expressed in the widely read and influential books
of Robert Ardrey and Konrad Lorenz. Ardrey's books are *African
Genesis* (Atheneum, 1961), and *The Territorial Imperative* (Atheneum, 1966). Lorenz's book is *On Aggression* (Harcourt, Brace &
World, 1966). In these books the authors argue that man is by
instinct an aggressive creature, and it is this innate propensity to
violence that accounts for individual and group aggression in man.
This Hobbesian view of human nature is not new; it is possibly
older than the doctrine of Original Sin, and was widely prevalent
during the reign of muscular Darwinism and its subsequent offspring Social Darwinism.[1] It was a view that was embraced by
Freud who, writing at the end of World War I, concluded that
"a powerful measure of desire for aggression has to be reckoned as
part of man's instinctual endowment. . . . *Homo homini lupus;*
who has the courage to dispute it in the face of all the evidence in
his own life and in history?"[2] Freud's postulation of a drive toward
death, *thanatos,* as an intrinsic part of human nature is well

---

[1] Ashley Montagu, *Darwin, Competition, and Cooperation.* New York: Schuman,
1952; Richard Hofstadter, *Social Darwinism in American Thought, 1860–1915.*
Boston: Beacon Press, 1961.
[2] Sigmund Freud, *Civilization and Its Discontents.* London: Hogarth Press, 1930.

known.[3] The death instinct, as it came to be known, has been largely repudiated by psychoanalysts, but the conception of such an instinct or drive toward destruction has lost none of its force in the minds of many people. Its revival, in the new garb given it in the writings of Ardrey and Lorenz, comes at a period in the history of man which renders the views expressed by such writers most acceptable to their lay readers.

The layman is bewildered. Two World Wars, the breakdown in political, public, and private morality, the ever-increasing crime rates, the development of a climate and a culture of violence, together with the consciousness of an apocalyptic realization of irreversible disaster, are quandaries enough to cause men to look desperately about them for some sort of an answer, for some explanation of the meaning, of the causes which seem to be leading man to destruction.

It is understandable that under such circumstances men will readily embrace an explanation having the appearance of plausibility, especially when that explanation is offered pretentiously, with at least the appearance of support from the apparatus of scientific learning, observation, discoveries, experiments, facts, and authorities. In addition to this, when the proponents of that explanation are able and eloquent writers, it is all the more easy for those who are not themselves authorities to be carried away by the arguments. What is almost certain to escape many readers, including some scientists, is that the apparatus of scientific learning, observations, experiments, and facts, however authoritative, do not speak for themselves but are always at the mercy of their interpreters. However thoroughly established the facts, their interpretation is always subject to human error, tendentiousness, and prejudice. Hence, the checks and controls that scientists from the relevant fields bring to bear upon the interpretation of the facts upon which they are experts, constitute the means and the measure by which such interpretations are judged. This is what has been done in the present volume in connection with the writings of Ardrey and Lorenz.

As the reader will be able to judge for himself, the experts have found the theories of Ardrey and Lorenz unsound. What is most serious is that Ardrey and Lorenz show themselves to be so en-

[3] Sigmund Freud, *Beyond the Pleasure Principle*. London: Hogarth Press, 1922.

amored of their own theories that they overlook or evade ~~bodies~~ of fact that do not support their theories. It is therefore not surprising that they often get the pieces of fact they choose to offer, as demonstrating their theories, twisted, or even wrong. It is to be hoped that the present volume will serve to put the record straight, to correct what threatens to become an epidemic error concerning the causes of man's aggression, and to redirect attention to a consideration of the real causes of such behavior.

It is very easy to accept the idea of an instinctive cause for man's aggression, for that explains everything. But what explains everything in fact explains nothing. There is an old English proverb, at least as old as the seventeenth century, which says, "Let him make use of instinct, who cannot make use of reason." I am not sure that it has quite the meaning intended here, but it will serve to make the point in much the same sense that John Stuart Mill intended when he observed, in 1848, that "Of all the vulgar modes of escaping from the consideration of the effect of social and moral influence on the human mind, the most vulgar is that of attributing the diversities of conduct and character to inherent natural differences."[4] If no other rational explanation appeals, or even when it does, instinct is likely to trump every other card in the pack because it appears to be so fundamental, so recondite, so all-embracing, and so simple. For these reasons, among others, the notion of "instinct" as an explanation of human aggression has ~~so~~ much greater an appeal than any other exegesis. To those who find such an explanation acceptable it makes little difference that for many years scientists have entertained such grave doubts concerning the existence of instincts in man, that for almost half a century fewer and fewer scientists have used the term in connection with man. The attack on the concept of instinct in man began in 1919 with the appearance of Knight Dunlap's article, "Are There Any Instincts?"[5] and was thoroughly discredited with the publi-

---

[4] John Stuart Mill, *Principles of Political Economy.*

[5] Knight Dunlap, "Are There Any Instincts?" *Journal of Abnormal and Social Psychology, 14:*307–11, 1919–20. See also L. L. Bernard, "The Misuse of Instinct in the Social Sciences," *Psychological Review, 28:*96–118, 1921; Ellsworth Faris, "Are Instincts Data or Hypotheses?" *American Journal of Sociology, 27:*184–96, 1921–22; Zing Yang Kuo, "Giving Up Instincts in Psychology," *Journal of Philosophy, 18:*645–64, 1921.

cation in 1924 of L. L. Bernard's fine work, *Instinct: A Study of Social Psychology*.[6] In spite of an attempt more than a decade ago to revive the idea of the existence of instincts in man [7] the notion has no scientific validity whatever.)

(The best known and most widely quoted definition of an instinct was that given by William McDougall in *An Introduction to Social Psychology,* first published in 1908. In this widely influential book an instinct was defined as "an inherited or innate psycho-physical disposition which determines its possessor to perceive, and to pay attention to, objects of a certain class, to experience an emotional excitement of a particular quality upon perceiving such an object, and to act in regard to it in a particular manner, or, at least, to experience an impulse to such action."[8] Definitions of instinct, whatever form they may have taken—and they have seemed almost infinitely varied—have widely tended to follow the essentials of McDougall's pattern. Tinbergen's rather elaborate ethological definition, for example, constitutes only one of many variations on the McDougallian theme. An instinct, according to Tinbergen, is "a hierarchically organized nervous mechanism which is susceptible to certain priming, releasing and directing impulses of internal as well as of external origin, and which responds to these impulses by coordinated movements that contribute to the maintenance of the individual and the species."[9]

(Essentially, we find that most definitions of *instinct* embody the same assumptions. The most common of these appear to be: (1) *innate* determiners of some kind which, (2), when affected by particular stimuli, (3), call into function certain neural, glandular, and muscular mechanisms, (4), that underlie particular patterns of behavior or even "psychological states." Such definitions of instinct are invariably based upon the study of behavior in "lower" animals, and not the behavior of man.) Tinbergen, for example, is properly cautious when he comes to touch upon the possibility of instincts in man. What has been proved in other animals, he writes, has not been proved in man.) "Further, different species have differ-

---

[6] L. L. Bernard, *Instinct: A Study in Social Psychology.* New York: Holt, 1924.

[7] Ronald Fletcher, *Instinct in Man.* New York: International Universities Press, 1957.

[8] William McDougall, *An Introduction to Social Psychology,* 14th ed., New York: Barnes & Noble, 1960, p. 25.

[9] N. Tinbergen, *The Study of Instinct.* Oxford: Clarendon Press, 1951, p. 112.

ent instincts. For instance, while many species have a parental instinct, others never take care of their offspring and hence probably do not have the corresponding neurophysiological mechanisms. . . ." Furthermore, "a species might lack a certain instinct because, having lost it relatively recently, it retained the nervous mechanism but not the required motivational mechanism. So long as we know nothing about such things, it would be as well to refrain from generalizations." [10]

That sounds a proper note of caution. But even Tinbergen's assumption that his interpretation of "instinct" holds for lower animals, calls for the most careful, skeptical examination. The truth is that the concept of "instinct" has assumed the form of a doctrine, and perhaps represents the outstanding example of reification in the whole realm of science, the employment of an abstraction as if it had a real existence. The revival of the abstraction "instinct" by Lorenz and Tinbergen in their studies of animal behavior has been thoroughly examined and their interpretation of the term rejected on strong grounds of evidence and theory.[11]

Rationalizing on the basis of insufficiently analyzed evidence (or both, together with procedures which distort the evidence) is a practice which is probably as old as man himself. This is a dangerous practice which is liable to produce pseudological arguments. Even scientists are not immune to it, especially when they become enamored of theories which tend to make them insensible to alternative interpretations of the facts.

The trouble is that many people confuse fact with theory. *Facts* are evidence; *theory* is interpretation of that evidence. Facts are reliable if they hold up in repetitions of investigations of their reality; a theory is valid if it offers the best possible interpretation of the facts—that is, the soundest and most logical.

For example, with respect to the problem of aggression we face two major questions. Question One concerns Lorenz's evidence for an "instinct" of aggression in lower animals. We ask: Is this evidence he offers reliable; does it include all of the important facts now available and relevant to behavior in lower animals; and how

10 Ibid.
11 See especially D. S. Lehrman, "A Critique of Konrad Lorenz's Theory of Instinctive Behavior," *Quart. Rev. Biol.*, 28:337–63, 1953.

validly does he interpret this evidence—for example, without appealing to authority or to personal prejudices, and so on? This is one question.

Question Two is: How well do the evidence and the argument that Lorenz offers for lower animals apply to man? Readers must accept the possibility that Lorenz's proffered answer to Question One is not valid; for example, that it is so misleading that his theory of aggression as innate is not really supported even for lower animals. If this is the case, and we think it is the case, anyone (e.g. Ardrey) who relies on Lorenz for an answer to Question One had better reconsider any arguments he bases on Lorenz.

Lorenz himself takes for granted (and abundantly rationalizes) his conclusion that he has answered Question One correctly. That is, he thinks he has demonstrated the soundness of his belief that "instinctive aggression" exists in lower animals. We doubt that he has done so, for reasons made clear in this book. Moreover, we hold that Lorenz has not demonstrated how any answer to Question One may bear on Question Two. This is not to say that a really valid answer to Question One could have some important bearing on Question Two. We agree with those writers who have stated that Lorenz's procedure of applying his doctrine of innate aggression in lower animals directly to man is naïve.

In the case of man it is possible to say that in spite of all attempts to saddle him with instincts, all such attempts have thus far failed.

The notable thing about *human* behavior is that it is learned. Everything a human being does as such he has had to learn from other human beings. From any dominance of biologically or inherited predetermined reactions that may prevail in the behavior of other animals, man has moved into a zone of adaptation in which his behavior is dominated by learned responses. It is within the dimension of culture, the learned, the man-made part of the environment that man grows, develops, and has his being as a behaving organism. Whatever other recondite elements may be involved in his behavior, and whatever the limits that his genetic constitution may set upon his learning capacities, this is the conclusion of the behavioral sciences—the sciences concerned with the study of the origins and causes of man's behavior. If anyone has any evidence to the contrary, let him bring it forth. That heredity plays a part in all human behavior is patently false, but that heredity plays a role in some human behavior can scarcely be doubted; but this is a very different thing from saying that any form of human behavior is determined by heredity.[12]

I have already discussed some of the probable reasons for the popularity of Ardrey's and Lorenz's explanations of the supposed causes of human aggression. There is yet another, perhaps the principal, reason for the popularity of works of this kind, including novels such as William Golding's *Lord of the Flies* [13] and Desmond Morris's recently published zoological study *The Naked Ape*,[14] which all serve to underscore that putative trait of human nature which our Victorian ancestors so charmingly called "innate depravity." In a world in which hostility and aggression seem to be a part of every man's nature, in which individual and group violence seem to constitute the incontrovertible evidence of the mark of Cain that every man carries within him, it is very gratifying to be told that this is indeed so; for those who are ready to grasp at such an explanation of human aggression it provides relief for that heavy burden of guilt most individuals carry about with them for being as they are. If one is born innately aggressive, then one cannot be blamed for being so. One can try not to be nasty, and even though nastiness does express itself one cannot be held responsible, for who can successfully resist the pressure of so powerful an "instinct" as aggression? Hence when books such as those of Ardrey and Lorenz appear they are welcomed with all the fervor of a sinner seeking absolution for his sins. Ardrey and Lorenz stand in a sort of apostolic succession to those who with millennial ardor have sought to restore the wicked and the unregenerate to the true faith. For is it not written in Romans 7:18–24:

> For I know that in me (that is, in my flesh,) dwelleth no good thing: for to will is present with me; but how to perform that which is good I find not.
>
> For the good that I would I do not: but the evil that I would not, that I do.

[12] See, for example, the studies in Jerry Hirsch (ed.), *Behavior-Genetic Analysis*. New York: McGraw-Hill, 1967.

[13] William Golding, *Lord of the Flies*. New York: Harcourt, Brace, 1954.

[14] Desmond Morris, *The Naked Ape*. New York: McGraw-Hill, 1968.

Now if I do that I would not, it is no more I that do it, but sin that dwelleth in me.

I find then a law, that, when I would do good, evil is present with me.

For I delight in the law of God after the inward man:

But I see another law in my members, warring against the law of my mind, and bringing me into captivity to the law of sin which is in my members.

O wretched man that I am! who shall deliver me from the body of this death?

Never was the question more eloquently and poignantly put. But most people, like Pontius Pilate in a similar situation, would not stay for an answer, but continued to seek an answer that was more congenial to them, one that promised absolution from the sin that held them captive. But for emancipation from that sin they would not look, for is it not written into the very flesh of man that that can never be?

It is this sort of thinking, so damaging, so pessimistic, so fettering of the human spirit, that is so dangerous because it diverts the focus of attention from the real causes of "sin," of aggression, and encourages a Jansenist view of the nature of the human condition. The evidence of scientific inquiry does not support this dismal view of human nature, still less does it provide any support for the idea of "innate depravity," whatever form that doctrine may take. Certainly the views of Ardrey and Lorenz concerning man's nature have no scientific validity whatever. It is our hope that the critique of those views presented in the pages which follow will serve to show why.

A.M.

8 June 1968
Princeton, N.J.

Man and Aggression

M. F. ASHLEY MONTAGU

The New Litany of "Innate Depravity," or Original Sin Revisited

It is said that when the Bishop of Worcester returned from the Oxford meeting of the British Association in 1860, he informed his wife, at tea, that the horrid Professor Huxley had declared that man was descended from the apes. Whereupon the dear lady is said to have exclaimed, "Descended from the apes! Let us hope it is not true, but if it is, let us pray that it will not become generally known."

It would seem that the last forty years of anthropological research and discovery in the field and in the laboratory, taken together with the findings of the behavioral sciences, place us in much the same position as the Bishop's lady, for while the findings of these disciplines are wholly opposed to the deeply entrenched view that man is an innately aggressive creature, most people tend to dismiss these findings out of hand or ridicule them as a rather eccentric idealistic heterodoxy, which do not deserve to become generally known. In preference to examining the scientific findings they choose to cast their lot with such "authorities" as William Golding who, in his novel *Lord of the Flies*,[1] offers a colorful account of the allegedly innate nastiness of human nature, and Robert Ardrey who, in *African Genesis*[2] and more recently in *The Territorial Imperative*,[3]

From *The Human Revolution*, Bantam Books, 1967. Reprinted by permission. New material added by author, 1968.

3

similarly seeks to show that man is an innately aggressive creature.

The first part of *African Genesis* is devoted to a demonstration, which the author brings off quite convincingly and with éclat, of the validity of Professor Raymond Dart's claims for an osteodontokeratic culture among the australopithecines. It is in the second part that Mr. Ardrey makes one of the most remarkable extrapolations from the first part I have ever encountered in any work. Mr. Ardrey argues that since the australopithecines made use of tools, and employed some of them as implements with which to bash in the skulls of baboons, the australopithecines were therefore "killers," and that *therefore* human beings are "killers" by nature! Mr. Ardrey's book constitutes, perhaps, the most illuminating example of the manner in which a man's prejudices may get in the way of his reason and distort his view of the evidence. Mr. Ardrey refers to some of his early personal experiences of violence which convinced him of the murderousness of human nature. Hence, when through the distorting glass of his prejudgments he looks at a tool it becomes not simply a scraper but a weapon, a knife becomes a dagger, and even a large canine tooth becomes "the natural dagger that is the hallmark of all hunting mammals," while in "the armed hunting primate" it becomes "a redundant instrument." "With the advent of the lethal weapon natural selection turned from the armament of the jaw to the armament of the hand."

But the teeth are no more an armament than is the hand, and it is entirely to beg the question to call them so. Virtually all the members of the order of primates, other than man, have large canine teeth, and these animals, with the exception of the baboons, are predominantly vegetarians, and it is because they are vegetarians that they require large canine teeth; that such teeth may, on occasion, serve a protective purpose is entirely secondary to their main function, which is to rip and shred the hard outer coverings of plant foods. Primates are not usually belligerent unless provoked, and the more carefully they are observed the more remarkably revealing do their unquarrelsomeness and cooperativeness become. The myth of the ferocity of "wild animals" constitutes one of Western man's supreme rationalizations, for it not only has served to "explain" to him the origins of his own aggressiveness, but also to relieve him of the responsibility for it—for since it is "innate," derived from his early apelike ancestors, he can hardly, so he rationalizes, be blamed for it! And some have gone so far as to add that nothing can be done about it, and that therefore wars and juvenile delinquents, as Mr. Ardrey among others tells us, will always be with us! From one not-so-minor error to another Mr. Ardrey sweeps on to the grand fallacy.

At this point it needs to be said that Mr. Ardrey's views are firmly based on and derived from those of Professor Raymond Dart, who in an article entitled, "The Predatory Transition from Ape to Man," [4] published in 1953, argued that man's animal ancestry was carnivorous, predatory, and cannibalistic in origin, and went on to add that "The blood-bespattered, slaughter-gutted archives of human history from the earliest Egyptian and Sumerian records to the most recent atrocities of the Second World War accord with early universal cannibalism, with animal and human sacrificial practices or their substitutes in formalized religions and with the world-wide scalping, head-hunting, body-mutilating and necrophiliac practices of mankind in proclaiming this common bloodlust differentiator, this predaceous habit, this mark of Cain that separates man dietetically from his anthropoidal relatives and allies him rather with the deadliest of Carnivora." [5]

Mr. Ardrey puts this in the following words: "The human being in the most fundamental aspects of his soul and body is nature's last if temporary word on the subject of the armed predator. And human history must be read in these terms."

In furtherance of this argument "tools" for Mr. Ardrey are not only identified as "weapons," but, he goes on to imply, nay, indeed, he states, "that when any scientist writes the word, 'tool,' as a rule he refers to weapons. This is a euphemism" (p. 306).

Perhaps this opportunity should be taken to assure Mr. Ardrey that when scientists write the word "tool" they mean exactly what they say, and that euphemisms are not, as Mr. Ardrey says, "normal to all natural science" (p. 306). Some tools may be used as weapons and even manufactured as such, but most tools of prehistoric man, from his earliest days, were most certainly not designed primarily to serve as weapons. Knives were designed to cut, scrapers to scrape, choppers to chop, and hammers to hammer. That such tools could be used as weapons is true, but to serve as weapons was not their primary purpose nor the reason for which they were devised.

"Man," Mr. Ardrey tells us, "is a predator whose natural instinct is to kill with a weapon" (p. 316). But man has no instincts, and if he had, they could hardly include the use of weapons in their psychophysical structure.

Early man's hunting, according to Mr. Ardrey, was due to instinctive belligerence, not to the hunger for food. "When the necessities of the hunting life encountered the basic primate instincts, then all were intensified. Conflicts became lethal, territorial arguments minor wars. . . . The creature who had once killed only through circumstance now killed for a living" (p. 317). This was "the aggressive imperative."

The evidence does not support Mr. Ardrey's theories. Whatever "the basic primate instincts" may be, they are not what Mr. Ardrey implies. Indeed, when he forgets himself, he writes of "the non-aggressive, vegetarian primate," which is precisely what all primates tend to be. But Mr. Ardrey would have us believe the contrary: the basic primate instincts according to him are aggressive. And, of course, with the assumption of hunting as a way of life, these, according to him, would become intensified. But in previous pages, and at greater length elsewhere, I have given the evidence for the contrary view. This evidence renders Mr. Ardrey's interpretations quite unacceptable. Everything points to the non-violence of the greater part of early man's life, to the contribution made by the increasing development of cooperative activities, the very social process of hunting itself, the invention of speech, the development of food-getting and food-preparing tools, and the like. These facts are never once mentioned by Mr. Ardrey, except perhaps obliquely as a doctrine which scheming scientists have foisted upon an unsuspecting world. The truth is that Mr. Ardrey is arguing a thesis. It is the thesis of "innate depravity." It is an unsound thesis, and it is a dangerous one, because it perpetuates unsound views which justify, and even tend to sanction, the violence which man is capable of learning, but which Mr. Ardrey erroneously believes to be inherited from man's australopithecine ancestors.

When man hunts he is the predator and the hunted animal is the prey. But prehistoric man did not hunt for pleasure, in order to satisfy his "predatory instincts." He hunted for food, to satisfy his hunger, and the hunger of those who were dependent upon him. He did not hunt because he was a "killer," any more than contemporary men are "killers" who kill animals in abattoirs so that others may eat them. Prehistoric man was no more a "killer" than we are "killers" when we sit down at table to consume a chicken or a steak which, by proxy, someone else has "killed" for us. It would be interesting to know who are the "murderers," the men who are paid to slaughter the animals we eat, or we who pay the cashier at the supermarket? Or perhaps it is really the owner of the store in which we buy meat who is the "murderer," the "killer"? Prehistoric man hunted because he desired to live—*that* hardly makes him a killer, any more than our continuing in the habit of eating meat makes us killers.

When Mr. Ardrey admiringly presents us with *West Side Story* as a "vivid portrait of natural man," in which "we watch our animal legacy unfold its awful power," in the form of juvenile delinquents in their "timeless struggle over territory, as lunatic in the New York streets as it is logical in our animal heritage," we can only say, "in police parlance," that it is worthy of William Golding's *Lord of the Flies,* in which a similar view of the depravity of human nature is unfolded. In Golding's novel two groups of children, abandoned on an island, take to hunting each other to the death. This novel has a wide readership on American college campuses, and it has recently been made into a film. Its appeal to young people is not strange, for in the world of violence in which they live Golding's novel supplies them with an easy "explanation." I understand that the novel is used in some sociology courses as a good illustration of "innate depravity," of the alleged natural nastiness of man. It could hardly be expected to be otherwise.[6]

Mr. Ardrey has further elaborated his views in a book entitled *The Territorial Imperative,*[7] published in August 1966. In this work Mr. Ardrey endeavors to show that man's aggressiveness is based on his allegedly innate territorial nature. Man, he argues, has an innate compulsion to gain and defend exclusive territory, preserve or property. The territorial nature of man, he says, is genetic and ineradicable.

Mr. Ardrey devotes the greater part of his book to a discussion of territoriality in many different kinds of animals. He attempts to show that territoriality in animals is innately determined. The informed student of these matters would be interested in knowing why the evidence has not been considered which leads to the opposite conclusion. Mr. Ardrey writes that "The disposition to possess a territory is innate. . . . But its position and borders will be learned" (p. 25). Certainly it is biologically and socially valuable for many animals to possess their own special territory, and certainly there are strong drives in most animals to defend their territory against trespassers, but such drives are not necessarily innate. They may be learned in just the same way in which animals learn the position and borders of their territory. Territory is defined as an area defended by its occupant against competing members of the same species. But there are many animals that do not exhibit such behavior. The California ground squirrel, adult male long-tailed field mice, she-wolves, the red fox, the Iowan prairie spotted skunk, the northern plains red fox, and in the superfamily to which man belongs, the Hominoidea, the orang-utan, the chimpanzee, and the gorilla, as well as many other animals. As Bourlière has observed in his admirable book, *The Natural History of Animals,* "It would seem that territorial behavior is far from being as important in mammals as in birds." [8] Somehow, Ardrey manages to neglect to consider the significance of these many exceptional cases. And while he does mention the chimpanzee, he omits any reference to the orang-utan [9] and the gorilla. [10] On the naturally amiable chimpanzee's non-territoriality he comments, "The chimpanzee has demonstrated, I presume, that we must reckon on some degree of innate amity in the primate potential; but as I have indicated, it is a very small candle on a very dark night" (p. 222).

On the contrary, the non-territoriality of great apes constitutes, one would have thought, a very bright beacon in a cloudless sky, for if, as is evident, man's nearest collateral relatives are wanting in anything resembling an inborn territorial drive, it is highly improbable that any form of man was ever characterized by such a drive. Arguments based on fish, birds, and other animals are strictly for them. They have no relevance for man. "The otherwise admirable animal," the chimpanzee, is for Mr. Ardrey, "an evolutionary fail-ure" (p. 223), while the aggressive baboon is "an outrageous evolu-tionary success" (p. 222).

Apparently evolutionary failure or success is to be measured by the yardstick of population number. The baboons are many, the great apes are few and are threatened with extinction. There is little evidence that the great apes were ever numerous, but that they are today few in number and threatened with extinction is all too tragi-cally true. The diminishing numbers of these animals is due not to their lack of territoriality, but to the encroachments upon both their habitats and their lives by men with weapons against which they are utterly defenseless. No matter how highly developed their territorial sense might have been, they could never have withstood these on-slaughts.

What we are witnessing in Mr. Ardrey's "territorial imperative" is a revival in modern dress of the good old "Instinct of Property" which, together with such oddities as the "Instinct of Philoprogeni-tiveness" and other such curiosities were repudiated by scientists half a century ago.[11]

Mr. Ardrey deplores the rejection of "instinct" in man, and actu-ally goes so far as to suggest that "a party line" has appeared in American science designed to perpetuate the "falsehood" that in-stincts do not exist in man. Mr. Ardrey needs the concept of "open instincts," of innate factors, to support his theorizing. But that re-quirement constitutes the fatal flaw in his theory, the rift in the playwright's lute, for man is man because he has no instincts, be-cause everything he is and has become he has learned, acquired, from his culture, from the man-made part of the environment, from other human beings. Mr. Ardrey declines to accept that fact, being more enamored of his theories than he is of facts. This is rather a pity because he would serve himself and us all a great deal more worthily if he would only realize that a scientist is not interested in proving or in disproving theories, in believing or in disbelieving, but in discovering what *is*. Thomas Henry Huxley once remarked of Herbert Spencer that his idea of a tragedy was a beautiful theory killed by an ugly fact. In Mr. Ardrey's case the beautiful facts render his ugly theories otiose.

What is the explanation of the appeal such books have for so many people? Golding's novel is a rattling good story. Ardrey's books are excitingly written and hold the reader spellbound. But these qualities are not the secret of their appeal. What, then, is?

Such books are both congenial to the temper of the times and comforting to the reader who is seeking some sort of absolution for his sins. It is gratifying to find father confessors who will relieve one of the burdensome load of guilt we bear by shifting the responsibility for it to our "natural inheritance," our "innate aggressiveness."

If it is our "nature" to be what we are, if we are the lineal descendants of our "murderous" ancestors, we can hardly be blamed or blame ourselves for the sin of being little more than made-over apes. Our orneriness is explained, and so is the peccant behavior of children, juvenile delinquency, crime, rape, murder, arson, and war, not to mention every other form of violence. It is all simply explained: it is due to man's innate aggressiveness.

There is nothing new in all this. We have heard it before. During the latter half of the 19th century, and during the early part of the 20th century, this viewpoint formed the foundation for the doctrine of "Social Darwinism." It was implied in such ideas as "The Survival of the Fittest" and "The Struggle for Existence," and in such phrases as "The weakest go to the wall," "Competition is the life-blood of a nation," and the like.

Such ideas were not merely taken to explain, but were actually used to justify, violence and war. As General von Bernhardi put it in 1912, "War is a biological necessity . . . it is as necessary as the struggle of the elements in Nature . . . it gives a biologically just decision, since its decisions rest on the very nature of things." [12] One wonders what von Bernhardi would have said after the "biologically just" defeat of Germany in two World Wars? No doubt, the general would have had little difficulty in finding an "explanation."

The new liturgy of "innate aggression," as an explanation of man's proclivities to violent behavior, does not seek to justify that behavior, but by thus "explaining" it to point the direction in which we must proceed if we are to exercise some measure of control over it. Toward this end, Dr. Konrad Lorenz, one of the founders of the modern science of ethology—the study of behavior under natural conditions of life—has dedicated himself in his latest book, *On Aggression,* published in April 1966.[13]

In *On Aggression* Lorenz has set out his views at length. In many respects they parallel those of Ardrey.

Ardrey's and Lorenz's views suffer from the same fatal defect, namely, extrapolation from other animals to man.

Why do reasonable beings behave so unreasonably, asks Lorenz. And he answers, "Undeniably, there must be superlatively strong factors which are able to overcome the commands of individual reason so completely and which are so obviously impervious to experience and learning" (p. 237). "All these amazing paradoxes, however, find an unconstrained explanation, falling into place like the pieces of a jigsaw puzzle, if one assumes that human behavior, far from being determined by reason and cultural tradition alone, is still subject to all the laws prevailing in all phylogenetically adapted instinctive behavior. Of these laws we possess a fair amount of knowledge from studying the instincts of animals" (p. 237).

It is in these sentences that the flaws in Lorenz's argument are exhibited. First he assumes that man's frequent irrational behavior is phylogenetically based. Second, this enables him to conclude that the "laws" derived from the "study of the instincts of animals" are applicable to man.

There is, in fact, not the slightest evidence or ground for assuming that the alleged "phylogenetically adapted instinctive" behavior of other animals is in any way relevant to the discussion of the motive-forces of human behavior. The fact is, that with the exception of the instinctoid reactions in infants to sudden withdrawals of support and to sudden loud noises, the human being is entirely instinctless.

Those who speak of "innate aggression" in man appear to be lacking in any understanding of the uniqueness of man's evolutionary history. Unacquainted with the facts or else undeterred by them they insist on fitting whatever facts they are acquainted with into their theories. In so doing they commit the most awful excesses. But, as is well known, nothing succeeds like excess. Lorenz's assumptions and interpretations are typical.

"There is evidence" he writes, "that the first inventors of pebble tools—the African Australopithecines—promptly used their new weapon to kill not only game, but fellow members of their species as well" (p. 239). In fact there is not the slightest evidence for such a statement.

Lorenz continues, "Peking Man, the Prometheus who learned to preserve fire, used it to roast his brothers: beside the first traces of the regular use of fire lie the mutilated and roasted bones of Sinanthropus pekinesis himself" (p. 239).

Lorenz's interpretation of the "evidence" is one he shares with many others, but it is gravely doubted whether it is sound. The cracked bones of Peking man may represent the remains of individuals who died during a famine and who may well have been eaten by their surviving associates. This sort of thing has been known to occur among most peoples of whom we have any knowledge. There is, however, no record of any people, prehistoric, nonliterate, or anywhere in the annals of human history, who made a habit of killing their fellow men in order to dine off them. It is absurd to suggest that Peking man used fire "to roast his brothers." Does Lorenz seriously believe that Peking man made a practice of "roast brother"? As another possibility it does not appear to have occurred to Lorenz that, like some contemporary peoples, burning the corpse may have been Peking man's way of disposing of the dead.

Lorenz writes, "One shudders at the thought of a creature as irascible as all pre-human primates are, swinging a well-sharpened hand-ax" (pp. 241–242). For a serious student of animal behavior Dr. Lorenz appears to be singularly ill-informed on the temperaments of prehuman primates. It is not "irascibility" which is the term most frequently used to describe the temperaments of "prehuman primates" by those who know them best, but "amiability." The field studies of Schaller on the gorilla, of Goodall on the chimpanzee, of Harrisson on the orang-utan, as well as those of others,[14] show these creatures to be anything but irascible. All the field observers agree that these creatures are amiable and quite unaggressive, and there is not the least reason to suppose that man's prehuman primate ancestors were in any way different. Captured monkeys and apes in zoos and circuses are not the best examples from which to deduce the behavior of such creatures under natural conditions.

Lorenz writes of early man faced with "the counter-pressures of hostile and neighboring hordes" (p. 243). Again, there exists not the slightest evidence of hostility between neighboring hordes of early man. The populations of early man were very small, a few score or a few hundred individuals at most. "Neighboring hordes" would have been few and far between, and when they met it is extremely unlikely that they would have been any less friendly than food-gathering hunting peoples are today.

The hostile neighboring tribe," writes Lorenz, "once the target at which to discharge phylogenetically programmed aggression, has now withdrawn to an ideal distance, hidden behind a curtain, if possible of iron. Among the many phylogenetically adopted norms of human social behavior, there is hardly one that does not need to be controlled and kept on a leash by responsible morality" (p. 253).

And there we have it: man's aggressiveness is "phylogenetically programmed," and can be kept within bounds only by moral controls.

Lorenz knows a great deal about the behavior of animals, but with respect to man he apparently knows very little else that is not in the realm of nineteenth-century desk anthropology. Like Ardrey, he extrapolates his dubious interpretations of animal behavior to still more dubious conclusions concerning man.

Since all instincts, according to Lorenz, are characterized by "spontaneity," and it is this spontaneity which makes "the aggression drive" so dangerous, one would have thought that he would have provided the reader with some convincing examples of such spontaneous aggression in man. But all that Lorenz can do is to cite the "very exact psychoanalytical and psycho-sociological studies on Prairie Indians, particularly the Utes" of Sydney Margolin (p. 244). According to these "very exact" studies the Prairie Indians "led a wild life consisting almost entirely of war and raids," and that therefore, "there must have been an extreme selection pressure at work, breeding extreme aggressiveness." Since Doctors Omer Stewart and John Beatty have independently shown how utterly erroneous this account is of the Prairie Indians in general and of the Utes in particular,* it only needs to be remarked that Lorenz's

* See pages 103–10, 111–15 of the present volume.

example of spontaneous aggression in man has not a leg to stand upon, and that the alleged "excess of aggression drive" "may have produced changes in the hereditary pattern" (p. 244) of the Utes are statements which derive no support whatever from the facts.

But Lorenz chooses to see aggression his way. Nowhere, for example, does he deign to consider how other scientists have looked at aggression. He neglects, for example, to discuss the possibility that a considerable proportion of aggressive behavior represents a reaction to frustration.[15] Nor does he pay the least attention to the view that in many instances aggressive behavior is situational, provoked by situations and conditions which have nothing whatever to do with anything "phylogenetically" or otherwise "programmed" in the individual. As a general and outstanding example of the spontaneity of instinctive aggression in man Lorenz cites "militant enthusiasm" which can be "elicited with the predictability of a reflex" when the proper environmental stimuli are available (p. 272). The possibility that "militant enthusiasm" may be learned behavior is not even considered by Lorenz. Lorenz's declarative statements are no substitute for the hard evidence that militant enthusiasm, like every other kind of enthusiasm, is learned.

The roles of learning and experience in influencing the development and expression of aggression are largely ignored by Lorenz. Yet the evidence is abundant and clear, both for animals and man, that learning and experience play substantive roles in the history of the individual or of the group in relation to the development of aggression. Where aggressive behavior is unrewarded and unrewarding, as among the Hopi and Zuñi Indians, it is minimally if at all evident.

"Let dogs delight to bark and bite, it is their nature to." Lorenz, who has written a charming book on dogs,[16] feels it is the nature, too, of men. Is it? What is human nature?

What is most important to understand in relation to that question is man's unique evolutionary history, the manner in which an ape was gradually transformed into a man as he moved from a dimension of limited capacity for learning into an increasingly enlarging zone of adaptation in which he became entirely dependent upon learning from the man-made part of the environment, *culture,* for his development as a functioning human being; that his brain, far from containing any "phylogenetically programmed" determinants for behavior, is characterized by a supremely highly developed generalized capacity for learning; that this principally constitutes his innate *hominid* nature, and that he has to learn his *human* nature from the human environment, from the culture that humanizes him, and that therefore, given man's unique educability, human nature is what man learns to become as a human being.

As we trace the details of man's evolutionary history we see that it is with the development of culture that man's brain began to grow and develop in a simultaneous feedback interaction with culture as an organ of learning, retrieval, and intelligence. Under the selection pressures exerted by the necessity to function in the dimension of culture, instinctive behavior would have been worse than useless, and hence would have been negatively selected, assuming that any remnant of it remained in man's progenitors. In fact, I also think it very doubtful that any of the great apes have any instincts. On the contrary, it seems that as social animals they must learn from others everything they come to know and do. Their capacities for learning are simply more limited than those of *Homo sapiens*.

As Clifford Geertz has put it,

> "Recent research in anthropology suggests that the prevailing view that the mental dispositions of man are genetically prior to culture and that his actual capabilities represent the amplification or extension of these pre-existent dispositions by cultural means is incorrect. The apparent fact that the final stages of the biological evolution of man occurred after the initial stages of the growth of culture implies that "basic," "pure," or "unconditioned," human nature, in the sense of the innate constitution of man, is so functionally incomplete as to be unworkable. Tools, hunting, family organization, and, later, art, religion, and "science" molded man somatically; and they are, therefore, necessary not merely to his survival but to his existential realization. It is true that without men there would be no cultural forms; but it is also true that without cultural forms there would be no men.[17]

Given the limits set by his genetic constitution, whatever man is he learns to be.

Throughout the two million years of man's evolution the highest premium has been placed on cooperation, not merely *intra*group cooperation, but also upon *inter*group cooperation, or else there would be no human beings today.[18] Intra- or intergroup hostilities, in small populations, would have endangered the very existence of such populations, for any serious reduction in numbers would have made the maintenance of such populations impossible. There is not the slightest evidence nor is there the least reason to suppose that such conflicts ever occurred in human populations before the development of agricultural-pastoral communities, not much more than 12,000 years ago.

The myth of early man's aggressiveness belongs in the same class as the myth of "the beast," that is, the belief that most if not all "wild" animals are ferocious killers. In the same class belongs the myth of "the jungle," "the wild," "the warfare of Nature," and, of course, the myth of "innate depravity" or "original sin." These myths represent the projection of our *acquired* deplorabilities upon the screen of "Nature." What we are unwilling to acknowledge as essentially of our own making, the consequence of our own disordering in the man-made environment, we saddle upon "Nature," upon "phylogenetically programmed" or "innate" factors. It is very comforting, and if, somehow, one can connect it all with findings on greylag goslings, studied for their "releaser mechanisms," and relate the findings on fish, birds, and other animals to man, it makes everything all the easier to understand and to accept.

What, in fact, such writers do, in addition to perpetrating their wholly erroneous interpretation of human nature, is to divert attention from the real sources of man's aggression and destructiveness, namely, the many false and contradictory values by which, in an overcrowded, highly competitive, threatening world, he so disoperatively attempts to live. It is not man's nature, but his nurture, in such a world, that requires our attention.

REFERENCES

1. William Golding, *Lord of the Flies,* New York: Harcourt, Brace & Co., 1954.
2. Robert Ardrey, *African Genesis,* New York: Atheneum, 1961.
3. Robert Ardrey, *The Territorial Imperative,* New York, Atheneum, 1966.

4. Raymond A. Dart, "The Predatory Transition from Ape to Man," *International Anthropological and Linguistic Review,* vol. 1, 1953, pp. 201–8.
5. Ibid. pp. 207–8.
6. For a critical examination by various authors of Golding's thesis, see William Nelson (ed.), *William Golding's Lord of the Flies: A Source Book,* New York: Odyssey, 1963.
7. Robert Ardrey, *The Territorial Imperative.*
8. François Bourlière, *The Natural History of Animals,* New York: A. A. Knopf, 1954, pp. 99–100.
9. Barbara Harrisson, *Orang-Utan,* New York: Doubleday, 1963.
10. George Schaller, *The Mountain Gorilla: Ecology and Behavior,* Chicago: University of Chicago Press, 1963, and the same author's *The Year of the Gorilla,* Chicago: University of Chicago Press, 1964.
11. L. L. Bernard, *Instinct,* New York: Holt, 1924; Otto Klineberg, *Social Psychology,* New York: Holt, 1954, pp. 63–75; David Krech and Richard S. Crutchfield, *Theory and Problems of Social Psychology,* New York: McGraw-Hill, 1948.
12. Friedrich von Bernhardi, *Germany and the Next War,* New York: Longmans, 1912.
13. Konrad Lorenz, *On Aggression,* New York: Harcourt, Brace & World, 1966.
14. Jane Goodall, "My Life among Wild Chimpanzees," *National Geographic,* vol. 124, 1963, pp. 272–308; George B. Schaller, *The Mountain Gorilla;* Barbara Harrisson, *Orang-Utan;* Charles H. Southwick (ed.), *Primate Social Behavior,* Princeton, N.J.: Van Nostrand, 1963; Irven DeVore (ed.), *Primate Behavior,* New York: Holt, Rinehart & Winston, 1965; Allan M. Schrier, Harry F. Harlow & Fred Stollnitz (eds.), *Behavior of Nonhuman Primates,* 2 vols., New York: Academic Press, 1965.
15. John Dollard *et al., Frustration and Aggression,* New Haven, Yale University Press, 1935.
16. Konrad Lorenz, *Man Meets Dog,* Boston: Houghton Mifflin, 1955.
17. Clifford Geertz, "The Growth of Culture and the Evolution of Mind," in Jordan Scher (ed.), *Theories of the Mind,* New York: Free Press, 1962, p. 736.
18. Ashley Montagu, *Darwin, Competition and Cooperation,* New York: Schuman, 1952; Ashley Montagu, *The Human Revolution,* New York: Bantam Books, 1967.

S. A. BARNETT

On the Hazards of Analogies

Samuel Johnson once wrote that weekly reviewers do not read books, but "lay hold of a topic, and write chiefly from their own wits." He added: "monthly reviewers are duller men, and are glad to read the books through."

Johnson's comment came to mind on a reading of some of the early reviews of *On Aggression*. These discuss especially the similarities that Lorenz believes exist in animal and human behavior. Joseph Alsop, in the *New Yorker,* detects a conflict between "the ethologists" (that is, Lorenz), on the one hand, and psychoanalysts and social scientists on the other: the latter, he suggests, are likely to regard analogies between ourselves and other species as invalid. By contrast, Anthony Storr, a psychotherapist who writes for the *Sunday Times* of London, accepts Lorenz's views on geese and men without protest. But Arthur Koestler, in the London *Observer,* describes these views as a "lusty gallop on a hobby horse," which it would be churlish to grudge.

Unfortunately, this reviewer finds himself forced to be churlish: a book prominently reviewed by celebrated writers becomes important regardless of its intrinsic merits. The reviews mentioned (all by non-zoologists) agree on one thing: that at least Lorenz's accounts of animal behavior are authoritative and reliable. But *On*

From *Scientific American*, February 1967. Copyright © 1967 by Scientific American, Inc. Reprinted by permission. New material added by author, 1968.

Aggression does not in fact represent the methods or opinions current in ethology (the science of animal behavior).

The main theme is stated in the introduction: "behavioral science really knows so much about the natural history of aggression that it does become possible to make statements about the causes of much of its malfunctioning in man." First, then, let us examine the "natural history of aggression," as Lorenz describes it. In chapter 3, entitled "What Aggression Is Good For," we are told that "we can safely assume that the most important function of intra-specific aggression is the even distribution of the animals of a particular species over an inhabitable area." But should we assume this? Lorenz does not discuss the evidence. The members of many, perhaps most, species are distributed, not evenly, but in quite large groups, crowds, or herds. These include large hoofed mammals and ground-living apes. Of them, Lorenz writes, "intra-specific aggression plays no essential part in the 'spacing out' of the species." He adds that among the herds of hoofed mammals there are no territorial boundaries.

This unsupported statement contradicts the observations of several careful workers. In 1956 William Graf described the territorial behavior of the elk, *Cervus canadensis*. These animals make territorial marks by scraping the bark off trees and rubbing their faces in the scrape. Graf also refers to the similar behavior of the black-tailed deer, *Odocoileus hemionus*. In 1957 Carl B. Koford described the behavior of the vicuna, *Vicugna vicugna*, whose territorial defense depends largely on a characteristic posture, in which the head and tail are held high. More recently there have been accounts of territory in the reindeer, *Rangifer tarandus*, and the Uganda cob, *Adenota kob*. Still other examples could be cited.

Lorenz also tells us that, when birds assemble in flocks outside the breeding season, they "lack aggression." This bare statement certainly needs qualification. For example, A.W. Stokes has described, in great detail, antagonistic behavior among blue tits, *Parus caeruleus*, at a winter feeding station. The work by Stokes is particularly important (and unusual) in that it gives *quantitative* information on the effects of various postures on the behavior of the birds toward which these signals are directed.

Further examples of disregard of evidence come in the account of the social behavior of wild rats, to which Lorenz gives a chapter. He refers to the "bloody mass battles of the brown rat," *Rattus norvegicus*. Nothing of the sort appears in any of the detailed accounts of this species: in fact, serious clashes, when they do occur, consist of an attack by one rat on a single opponent; the latter does not fight back. Nor is there pair formation among wild rats, as Lorenz states: a female in oestrus accepts males indiscriminately; and males do not fight for females. (The only reference in the bibliography to work on rats is to a short paper on the interactions of "brown" and "black" rats. Encounters between these species are not bloody mass battles either.) Rats are also described as "models of social virtue," "cruel to their subordinates" and "horrible brutes." And they are said to transmit by tradition knowledge of the danger of poisons. The last statement is reminiscent of the simple tales, often written by clergymen in earlier times, about animal co-operation and its moral implications. (A popular story was of the old blind rat guided by a younger rat by means of a twig.)

In the same passage there is a reference to a similar transmission of pathfinding, and of recognition of foods and enemies. It is not clear in just which species these abilities are supposed to exist. There are evidently traditions of food choice within monkey colonies. As for pathfinding, young animals often follow older ones of their own species, but this has, as a rule, nothing to do with teaching or learning a tradition: there is a deep gulf between *following,* on the one hand, and *imitation* (or learning by observation) on the other. Any discussion of tradition in other species demands a critical account of this distinction, and of the kind of evidence needed before the existence of imitation may be accepted. This is perfectly practicable even in a popular work, but it is not attempted.

A curious digression concerns "the scene that must have taken place when, for the first time, two enemy Indians became friends by smoking a pipe together." The passage that follows is quite unrelated to anything known about the actual behavior of North American Indians.

Another passage more reminiscent of a moral tract than of ethology asks what has been learned "from the objective observation of animals" on the "ways intra-specific aggression assists the preservation of an animal species." Among the benefits, we are told, is that the community is so organized that "a few wise males, the 'senate,' acquire the authority essential for making and carrying out decisions for the good of the community." Among some species of Primates, elderly males do play a special part in social life: a single, senior baboon, *Papio,* for example, sometimes stops conflicts. But there is no authority for suggesting the existence of anything that can be called a senate (or legislature): not even male apes combine to regulate the conduct of their group, although an assault by an elderly baboon may be checked by a group of younger ones.

These examples of Lorenz's method illustrate a general difficulty which all scientific writers on behavior have to face: the use of colloquial language often makes exact description difficult, and rational explanation impossible. A lexical definition of "aggression," for example, is "assault." Yet the animal behavior commonly called "aggressive" consists usually of displays (or signals) which induce the withdrawal of intruders: it does not often involve a clash. (Even when there is actual contact, in natural conditions there is hardly ever serious injury.) The displays which lead to withdrawal may be postures, noises—such as bird song—or odors, and are often called threats. A lexical definition of "threat" is "a declaration of hostile intent." But it is difficult to give a precise meaning to a statement about what an animal *intends.* The word "threat" could be redefined as a signal which tends to induce withdrawal by a member of the same species. This at least allows the term to be used without ambiguity. An objection is that it ignores the performer's internal state. Among ourselves we think of threat as an index of anger or fear. To speak objectively about the counterparts of anger and fear in other species, we need to know something of the physiology of the behavior observed. This entails exact descriptions of electrical, chemical, and structural changes in the nervous system.

A start has been made in this difficult area, but it is not recognised by Lorenz. Instead, there are many references to "instinctual urges," "aggressive impulses," and similar undefined qualities. One of the difficulties in commenting on this book is indeed that key terms are not defined; much is ambiguous or obscure for this reason alone. The progress of science has depended on the rejection of what Newton called "occult qualities." Descriptions in science are of properties which can be reliably observed: "real is what can be measured." We no longer attribute the motion of the planets to angels; we do not "explain," or even name, the steady temperature of a mammal or a bird by an undefined "innate heat"; nor do we account for disease by the presence of demons.

In one passage Lorenz refers to the uselessness of terms such as "reproductive instinct" as explanations, but he repeatedly uses them elsewhere. The human "aggressive drive" is often mentioned; but, if this or any similar expression has a meaning, it is only that almost any human being *can* be provoked to violence. The crucial question is how the violence arises.

The lack of definition is especially awkward when Lorenz discusses patterns of behavior, such as displays, songs, modes of nest building, and so on, which are common to a whole species. Lorenz refers to these species-characteristic patterns as "hereditary," but this represents a confusion between heredity and development. Only *differences* between individuals may properly be called "hereditary." This confusion is an aspect of Lorenz's failure to take account of the development of behavior during the life history of each individual. Uniformity of behavior within a species has sometimes been thought to indicate complete stability in its development. This is now well known to be unjustified, and the concept of "innate behavior," as it appeared in ethological writings of, say, fifteen years ago, has been much modified.

Rhesus monkeys, *Macaca mulatta,* provide a notable example. These animals, like many others, have a status system or peck order within each group; whenever (as in natural conditions) there is a settled status system, conflict is, at most, trivial and harmless. Such social behavior might in the past have been called "instinctive." But if young monkeys are reared without other monkeys, they fail to develop the ability to take part in a stable society: when given companions later on, they are persistently "aggressive" in the sense that they frequently attack and injure others. These celebrated observations, made by Harry F. Harlow and his colleagues, are, of all studies of animal "aggression," the most relevant to Lorenz's theme. They illustrate the importance of studying how social (and antisocial) behavior *develops*. They are not mentioned in *On Aggression*.

There is much discussion of the *evolutionary* origin of behavior patterns. Great emphasis is put on the "triumph ceremony" of geese and other birds; the birds are described as if they were human beings. This ceremony, also called an "appeasement" activity, is seen in different forms in different species. Lorenz writes: "From this gradation we can form a picture of how, in the course of phylogeny, an anger-diverting gesture of embarrassment has developed into a bond which shows a mysterious relationship to that other bond between human beings and which seems to us the strongest and most beautiful on earth."

This and similar passages assume that evolutionary changes in behavior can be traced just as structural changes are traced, and that displays, such as those of courtship and territorial defense, have gradually evolved from other activities. For instance, birds take care of their body surfaces by preening. The displays of many species include movements which resemble preening, many of which show off in a striking way their characteristic feather patterns. Movements which originally had one function are supposed to have changed during evolution, so that they now have another as well. At the same time, the structures involved have evidently become more conspicuous, sometimes by acquiring bright colors. Julian Huxley named this hypothetical process "ritualization," and Lorenz makes many confident, dogmatic assertions about it. The workers who have contributed most in this field are Niko Tinbergen and his pupils. Tinbergen has written: "Comparative description of signals . . . [has] given us an idea of their evolutionary orgin and . . . leads to a description of their alleged ritualization. Assuming that our reasoning has been correct, can we guess what selection pressures must have been responsible for ritualization? The paucity of experimental work on survival value renders such guesses doubly hazardous." This cautious, critical statement represents the actual position among research workers on behavior today.

There are passages in *On Aggression* about stereotyped behavior in which the development of the behavior of an individual seems to be regarded as the same as evolutionary change in behavior due to natural selection. For instance, there are many rituals in human behavior which we call "superstitious," and in obsessional neurosis, induced by an unfavorable early environment, they become excessive. Lorenz writes of obsessional behavior and of the fixed action patterns of animals: "all these phenomena are related"; and he states: "all human art primarily developed in the service of rituals"; characteristically, instead of discussing the difficult problems raised by these proposals, he precedes ·the last-quoted statement with the words, "There is hardly a doubt that. . . ."

The emphasis on the stereotyped behavior of species other than man, and the neglect of behavior which can be readily altered by experience, is especially strange when the aim is to throw light on human behavior. Man is the one species whose social behavior (except in infancy) does *not* depend on a uniform set of social signals: all our customs, including language, depend on the training we receive in our own family or community. Hence arises the immense diversity of *mores* within the single species, *Homo sapiens*. Yet Lorenz writes: "human social behavior, far from being determined by reason and cultural tradition alone, is still subject to all the laws prevailing in all phylogenetically adapted instinctive behavior."

This statement is made without supporting argument—unless analogies constitute an argument. The great debate that has long raged on this sort of question is acknowledged only in a few statements such as: "The completely erroneous view that animal and human behavior is predominantly reactive and that, even if it contains any innate elements at all, it can be altered to an unlimited extent by learning, comes from a radical misunderstanding of certain democratic principles: it is utterly at variance with these principles to admit that human beings are not born equal and that not all have equal chances of becoming ideal citizens." Yet in fact there is no school of thought which states that animal, or even human, behavior can be altered to an unlimited extent by learning; and people who work for social justice do not say that all are born equal, but only that all should have equivalent opportunities to develop their abilities to the full. Lorenz may look back nostalgically to "the good old days when there was still a Habsburg monarchy and there were still domestic servants"; but this does not justify him in ascribing to his opponents opinions they do not hold.

What, then, are Lorenz's proposals on the causes and treatment of human "aggression"? What revelation has he in store for his readers? One is that there should be more international sport. This widely acceptable suggestion has often been made without benefit of ethology; which is not surprising, since—as Lorenz himself points out—sport is "specifically human." Lorenz does not, however, discuss whether there is evidence that it would reduce other kinds of conflict between nations or individuals. Another suggestion is that there should be more art, science, and medicine—the pursuits of truth, beauty, and healing; this, of course, is still more readily acceptable, since it has been a familiar notion for several thousand years. We are also urged to laugh more, and to love each other indiscriminately. The last recommendation perhaps accounts for the following sentence: "Not even the most ruthlessly daring demagogues have ever undertaken to proclaim the whole art of an enemy nation or political party as entirely worthless." It would be more appropriate if Lorenz had reminded his younger readers of the attempt by the Nazis, between 1933 and 1945, to destroy, not only the German Jewish community, but also the whole of Jewish culture.

The sentence last quoted strongly suggests that Lorenz lives in a private world, insulated from the real one. The same applies to his prinicipal recommendation for further research. "I believe—and human psychologists, particularly psychoanalysts, should test this—that present-day civilized man suffers from insufficient discharge of his aggressive drive." Never mind now that "aggressive drive" is not defined. This and similar notions have been debated among medical men and psychologists for several decades, and are the subject of a substantial literature, none of which is mentioned by Lorenz. The late Karen Horney, a leader of a prominent psychiatric school which especially emphasises this aspect of psychopathology, has written of "the neurotic person's need for indiscriminate supremacy."

Still more to the point is the research which has been done on the developmental psychology of the bully. In the 1940s H. V. Dicks produced convincing evidence that the personalities of the brutal, bigoted German soldiers, who formed a substantial minority of the Reichswehr, were products of families in which the father was a tyrant and the mother submerged. T. W. Adorno and his colleagues independently published a longer and celebrated work, *The Authoritarian Personality,* which extended and confirmed this analysis. On the development of "aggression" in childhood, Lorenz has little to say except for a reference to "countless unbearably rude [American] children" who, he tells us, were a product of the view that children ought to be "spared all disappointments and indulged in every way."

Being a dull man, in Samuel Johnson's classification, I have "read the book through" more than once. On each reading more self-contradictions, confusions, and questionable statements have emerged. How much more acceptable would have been an unpretentious account of actual behavior! It is sad that so much talent should have been misapplied in this fashion. As it is, since *On Aggression* is presented as authoritative at least on animal behavior, it is liable to bring ethology into disrepute with critical readers, and also to mislead students and laymen. But the scope and implications of the book are far wider. It makes statements on two crucial features of our existence: the growth of social behavior in children, and the prevention of violence and war. These are not topics in which loose thinking can be accepted with a tolerant shrug: such work should be based on a respect for facts, for logic and for the researches of others. Instead, the method of *On Aggression* is essentially anti-rational. This method should be repudiated by all scholars—indeed, by all responsible people.

GEOFFREY GORER

Man Has No "Killer" Instinct

One of the most persistent and widespread beliefs about "human nature" held by men of goodwill in most of the advanced societies in the world is that human beings are "naturally" peaceful and gentle, considerate of their fellow human beings and unwilling to hurt or kill them save under the (assumedly) exceptional conditions of war.

This belief in the essential gentleness of "human nature" can only be maintained by a wilful blindness that refuses to recognize the evidence which history, social anthropology, the daily newspapers and television so constantly provide of man's willingness to hurt and kill his fellows, and to take pride and pleasure in so doing.

In recent months we have read detailed accounts and seen gruesome pictures of Ibos and Hausas gleefully slaughtering one another in Nigeria, of massacres of Indonesians and Chinese in Java and other islands of the archipelago, of Chinese youngsters with red armlets self-righteously humiliating their elders, not to mention both sides in Vietnam. If we try to console ourselves by claiming that most of these slaughters and humiliations were the acts of people who were not civilized and not Christian, this consolation should be short-lived. The Boers and white Rhodesians claim Christian justification for the ill-treatment of their fellow citizens with darker skins; the pictures of the school at Grenada, Miss., are surely not forgotten; and no recorded "uncivilized" nation has equaled the systematic humiliation and slaughter practiced by Christian Germany and her allies a bare generation ago.

All known societies make a distinction between murder—the killing of a member of one's own group—and the killing of outsiders. We can understand murder for jealousy or gain or safety, however much we reprobate and punish it; we think it "rational." But when somebody kills without a "rational" motive—nurses in a dormitory, students from a university tower, policemen in a street—we are puzzled, disturbed and fascinated. The murder of eight nurses or three policemen will hold our attention over longer periods and with more intensity than the slaughter of masses of Javanese.

Contemporary psychological science is at a loss to account for people killing one another without a "rational" motive, according to our standards; an implicit hypothesis in all Western thinking, both scientific and popular, is that man has built-in instincts against killing except under extreme provocation. When people in our own societies kill without a "good reason" we tend to use the term "psychopath"; but this is really a scientific-sounding confession of ignorance and impotence.

Sometimes this pseudo-explanation is applied to killers in other societies; but more frequently the Malayan term "running amok" is used. In Malaya, and some other societies, individuals may suddenly start killing strangers, and amok is the Malayan term for this kind of behavior. This is, however, a description, not an explanation.

Some people reject the hypothesis that man is naturally peaceable and instead, invoke the hypothesis of a "killer instinct" as an aspect of man's hereditary endowment. This "instinct" is held to be normally under strong restraint in "civilized societies" but capable of erupting in "psychopathic" individuals and nearer the surface in "savage" societies. Were there evidence for such an "instinct" it would offer a sort of explanation for the joy of killing, for which there is such plentiful evidence; but I will argue that this is an unnecessary hypothesis.

The most important statement, almost without question, about this aspect of human nature made in this century is that contained in the recent book of the ethologist Konrad Lorenz, translated into English under the title, "On Aggression." He shows that all the carnivores, the mammals which kill other species for their food, have innate inhibitions (instincts, if the term be preferred) against killing members of their own species, with two exceptions—rats and men. The animals with potentially lethal teeth, claws or horns can be automatically stopped from pressing an attack on a fellow member of the species by signs of submission, either flight or some physical analogue to raising the hands or showing the white flag. Once the species-specific signs of submission are made, the attacker automatically halts; he literally *cannot* kill his defeated rival.

Dr. Lorenz argues that there is an evolutionary connection between the large carnivores' lethal physical equipment and the innate inhibitions against using this physical equipment on fellow members of the same species. In comparison, man is physically ill-equipped; his teeth and nails are not adapted to killing large animals of other species; and even his strong and clever hands could seldom be used on healthy beasts. It has indeed been argued that very early man, away from the seacoasts, relied on carrion for his protein. Since man is so physically ill-equipped for killing, he did not acquire the built-in inhibitions against killing other men as part of the evolutionary protection of the species, as wolves or tigers did for their co-specifics. And then he invented weapons.

To avoid confusion, it should be emphasized that for all carnivores, including man, killing other species of animals for food is innately of a different nature from killing members of the same species for rivalry or jealousy or pleasure. In animals, there is no connection between hunting and ferocity toward members of their own species; ethology gives no support to the arguments of tender-minded human beings that man would be less ferocious if he abstained from eating meat.

The Latin proverb, *homo homini lupus*—man is a wolf to man—has been taken over by nearly every society which derives its customs, laws or language from ancient Rome. This is a libel on the wolf, which is a gentle animal with other wolves. Ethologically more appropriate would be *homo homini mus rattus*—man is a rat to man—for, exceptionally among carnivores, rats do sometimes kill other rats. In his mating and child-rearing patterns, in his vision, and in some other aspects, man resembles birds more than he does other mammals; but in his treatment of his own species there is an uncomfortably close analogy with rats.

Rats live in packs or hordes; and (still following Dr. Lorenz) they do not fight seriously with, much less kill, members of the same pack. But they are quite merciless to members of alien packs; they kill them slowly and painfully and (if one wishes to be anthropomorphic) they seem to get pleasure from so doing. They share our lack of built-in inhibitions against killing members of the same species.

The analogy with human beings is almost total. Human beings also live in packs (in most cases the pack is the society) and the killing of other members of the pack is always forbidden (save, occasionally, under carefully defined rules) and typically subject to very severe sanctions; but this ban and these sanctions do not usually apply to members of other packs. As is well known, very many primitive tribes have only a single word to designate members of the tribe and human beings; they alone are fully human, members of other packs are (so to speak) subhuman, and killing them is not murder. This primitive type of rat-thinking is never far below the surface, even among the civilized and sensitive.

Where human beings differ from rats is in their very varying definitions of who shall be included within the pack. Usually, the pack is the society or tribe, people who speak the same language (typically unique to the tribe) and between whom real or supposititious bonds of kinship can be traced; but there are variants in both directions.

The smallest packs known to me are those described by Dr. and Mrs. Ronald M. Berndt, who studied four contiguous language groups in the Eastern Highlands of New Guinea. Here the people one should not kill are certain specified kinfolk and a few relations of one's wife or wives. Everyone else, irrespective of ancestry or language, was fit prey for the "deadly game" of death, for only by killing can a man earn power and prestige. The dead were eaten and, in the case of women, raped either before or after death.

The only reason why these packs had not exterminated one another before the Australians pacified the area a bare decade ago is that they practiced a policy of preservation of human game. They seldom killed more than they could eat, and left the temporarily weak in peace to breed. The gleeful, guiltless accounts that Dr. and Mrs. Berndt gathered from the participants in these orgies of slaughter, cannibalism and rape read like a nightmare vision of human savagery.

New Guinea also contains one of the relatively few tribes described by anthropologists in whom the joy of killing seems to be completely absent. These are the Arapesh, studied by Dr. Margaret Mead and Dr. Reo Fortune. They will be discussed in more detail subsequently.

For most of humanity, the tribe is the unit within which killing is considered murder, and outside which killing may be a proof of manhood and bravery, a pleasure and a duty. Such killing may be done by individuals—head-hunters, scalp-collectors, as part of a vendetta or raid—or by groups; in the latter case the killing is called "warfare." The differences in quality and scope between tribal warfare and modern war between nation-states are so great that it might be useful if different words were used for the two activities.

The nation-state was invented after the Neolithic revolution, less than 10,000 years ago; and this is a very short period in man's evolutionary history. One of the advantages of the nation-state is that it greatly extended the area within which killing would be murder; a number of tribes were brought under the same law and equally protected from mutual slaughter. This amalgamation is not now an easy one, as the sad condition of contemporary Nigeria or Indonesia demonstrates; and it probably was no less difficult in the past. There are no reliable contemporary records of the establishment of the first nation-states, mostly along the great rivers of Asia and North Africa; by the time adequate historical records commence, a dominant group had succeeded in preserving peace among the component tribes. The pack was successfully extended to include and protect most of the inhabitants of a given geographical area, even though slaves and captives were usually excluded.

The nation-state is really the last successful human invention for extending the size of the pack, within which killing is murder. In the past 4,000 years a number of religions have been founded which would include all believers inside the pack; but no religion has commanded worldwide allegiance; and regularly the outcasts, infidels, untouchables, heathen or heretics could all be humiliated or killed with added pleasure and self-righteousness, because they were members of the devil's pack.

The founders of the great world religions, Gautama Buddha, Jesus, Lao-Tzu, Mohammed, all seem to have striven for a world-wide brotherhood of man; but none of them could develop institutions which would include the enemy, the unbeliever, and give him the same protection from anger, hatred and the lust for killing which they decreed within their own congregations.

Within the last century and a half, various millennial ideologies—democracy, Socialism, the Communist internationals, the United Nations—have taken over the goal of the traditional religions: the establishment of a world-wide brotherhood of man, a single pack. They have been no more successful than their predecessors in protecting the enemy, the unbeliever, from the horrible results of righteous anger.

In recent centuries, most men of goodwill have at least paid lip-service to the ideal of a universal brotherhood with equal protection for all, whatever might be their actual behavior or that of their compatriots. But this century has seen a most sinister recrudescence of rat-pack ideology, in which human status is denied to all persons who do not share one's hypothetical ancestry or visible skin color: Fascism, Nazism, white supremacy, black power all justify hatred and contempt for those outside the pack; and recent history shows how easily, how very easily, this justified hatred and contempt develop into humiliation, torture and killing.

The evidence could be endlessly multiplied to demonstrate that man, as a species, has no inhibitions against killing his fellow men who do not belong to the same pack, however the pack may be defined, and often gets intense pleasure and a sense of pride from so doing. But to admit this is not the same as positing a "killer instinct" as part of man's hereditary endowment. There is no logical reason for hypothesizing such an instinct, and indeed some arguments, to be advanced shortly, against doing so.

Because men have no innate instinctual inhibitions against hurting and killing other members of their species, this offers some human beings a potential source of intense pleasure, as do incest, homosexuality and other sexual deviations. Man has no built-in inhibitions against these sources of pleasure either; did he possess them, laws would be unnecessary. Whether any of these pleasures will be sought, how frequently, and by whom, depends on the values of a specific society at a given time and the vicissitudes of individual lives.

Because man can and does gain intense pleasure from humiliating, hurting and killing his fellows, the speculative novels of the Marquis de Sade are extremely important documents, whatever their literary qualities. Save in a directly sexual situation (when he relished flagellation), de Sade was an affectionate, humane and very courageous man. In his 13-year-long solitary confinement he looked without flinching into the deepest recesses of his unconscious fantasies and reported, in fictional form, the pleasures to be derived from the unfettered exercise of power over one's fellow men and women.

De Sade linked these pleasures with the pleasures of sex; this was the only metaphor which contemporary science made available to him and it was congenial to his temperament. Even so, there are many episodes in the novels when power is used for its own sake— power to humiliate, hurt or kill—without any overt sexual gratification. De Sade wished to portray "the spasms of man's loathsome heart and fearful passions" because he was convinced that only by acknowledging the truth about human nature, as he saw it, could a safe and just society be built.

Classical psychoanalysis has in good part confirmed de Sade's pessimistic diagnosis of "man's loathsome heart." Freud always maintained the central position in his theory of the Oedipus complex; and the little Oedipus had murder in his heart, the killing of his father—a point which many contemporary psychoanalysts tend to gloss over. According to the findings of the late Melanie Klein and her followers, the inchoate hatred and rages of very young children produce wishes which, when translated into verbal metaphors, parallel the fantasies of de Sade: cannibalism, poisoning, evisceration, castration, murder.

The history of civilized nations in the century and a half since de Sade's death also confirms his pessimistic diagnosis of human behavior. Although he placed no bounds on his imagination, we have been witnesses to far greater horrors than de Sade could dream of;

man can be an even more savage monster than he guessed. It is possible that, had de Sade's diagnosis of human potentialities been taken consistently into account, the fanatics, torturers and murderers would have had less impunity in the indulging of their fearful passions.

There are, however, a few rays of hope, a few societies where men seem to find no pleasure in dominating over, hurting or killing the members of other societies, where all they ask is to be at peace and to be left in peace. These societies are, of course, small, weak, technologically backward, and living in inaccessible country; only so could they survive the power-seeking of their uninhibited neighbors.

Among these gentle societies are the Arapesh of New Guinea, mentioned earlier; the Lepchas of Sikkim in the Himalayas (whom I studied); and, most impressive of all, the pygmies of the Ituri rain-forest in the Congo, studied by Colin Turnbull. These small societies (there are several others) living in the most inaccessible deserts and forests and mountains of four continents, have a number of traits in common, besides the fact that they do not dominate over, hurt or kill one another or their neighbors, though they possess the weapons to do so. Many of them, including the pygmies and the Lepchas until a couple of generations ago, rely almost exclusively on hunting for their protein food.

What seem to me the most significant common traits in these peaceful societies are that they all manifest enormous gusto for concrete physical pleasures—eating, drinking, sex, laughter—and that they all make very little distinction between the ideal characters of men and women, particularly that they have no ideal of brave, aggressive masculinity.

Men and women have different primary sexual characteristics—a source of endless merriment as well as of more concrete satisfactions—and some different skills and aptitudes. No child, however, grows up with the injunctions, "All real men do . . . " or "No proper woman does . . . ," so that there is no confusion of sexual identity: no cases of sexual inversion have been reported among them. The model for the growing child is of concrete performance and frank enjoyment, not of metaphysical symbolic achievements or of ordeals to be surmounted. They do not have heroes or martyrs to emulate or cowards or traitors to despise; their religious life lacks significant personalized gods and devils; a happy, hard-working and productive life is within the reach of all.

As far as the history of these small tribes can be reconstructed, they have always chosen to retreat into ever more inaccessible country rather than stand their ground and fight with invaders. There is no reason to suppose that their psychological or physiological potentialities are different from those of their more aggressive neighbors, but their values certainly are; for them peace and the absence of quarreling and jealousy are far more important than a reputation for bravery and virility. And while the tribes are not broken up, it is likely that these values will continue to prevail. When the tribes are broken, individuals, unsupported by the traditional ethics, might easily revert to rat-pack mentality. Save that they have so far survived, these small tribes have not been conspicuously successful in the struggle for existence and terrain against more ruthless neighbors. Nevertheless, they may offer a paradigm of ways to diminish the joy of killing in the uninhibited human race.

By contrast, the cannibals in the New Guinea Highlands have a highly aggressive ideal of masculinity; and so, in general, do all the peoples who prize the martial virtues and self-righteously kill their enemies or their "inferiors." The New Guinea Highlanders frankly enjoy sex, especially if it approximates to rape; but many other martial societies repudiate all sensual pleasure as unworthy of a Real Man. If our gods and heroes are killers—Lords of Hosts, warriors, successful revolutionaries—and if masculinity is demonstrated by the willingness to give and take "punishment," then the joy of killing is always likely to re-emerge.

It seems possible that the youth international, which has developed nearly the whole world over in the last generation, has inarticulately sensed the necessity to redefine the concepts of a "real man" and "a true woman" if we are not to destroy ourselves completely. The long hair, dandified dress and pleasantly epicene features (which so infuriate their elders) are a physical repudiation of the ideal of aggressive masculinity which has been traditional in all their societies in recent generations, and which is still maintained by the conventional and the neo-Fascists (white supremacists, Empire loyalists, Birchites and the like) in the same societies.

Even idiotic slogans such as "Make love, not war" (as if the two activities had ever been incompatible!) and the use of drugs make the same point. Mankind is safer when men seek pleasure than when they seek the power and the glory.

If the members of the youth international—the beats and the swingers, the *provos* and the *stilyagi*—maintain the same scale of values and the same sex ideals 20 years hence when they themselves are middle-aged and parents, then they may, just possibly, have produced a permanent change in the value systems and sex roles of their societies, which will turn the joy of killing into an unhappy episode of man's historic past, analogous to human sacrifice, which ascribed joy in killing to the gods also.

The attempts to devise a social unit more inclusive than the nation-state, a brotherhood of man, have all been unsuccessful to date. It is just possible that the youth international, with its emphasis on shared sensual pleasure and its repudiation of the ideal of truculent "manliness," may succeed where the grandiose schemes of idealists have always failed. For man has no "killer instinct"; he merely lacks inhibitions.

SALLY CARRIGHAR

War Is Not in Our Genes

There are still men and women living who can remember the horror which greeted Darwin's theory that we are "descended from apes." That phrase probably accounted in part for the revulsion because "descended from" was generally used in a more personal way—"I am descended from Scottish ancestors," that is, I am one of them, I am like them. Darwin meant, of course, "We have evolved from apes," with apes standing in for the whole range of evolved animals, but the unfortunate phrase had caught on.

That we have *evolved* from apes—and are, therefore, obviously different from them—is an unemotional, scientific assertion, harmless enough, it would seem, except that it does leave Adam and Eve stranded without progeny and raises an unresolved question about men's souls. If each human being has been created with his own unique soul, then so have all animals—wolves, rabbits, mice, water bugs. To many people that thought was, and still is, intolerable, although the concept does not seem very difficult if one thinks of soul as *life,* the bit of animation temporarily lent from the great source of all life.

The first, grudging acceptance of evolution was in connection with physical structures: it was hard for anyone to deny such evidence as the development of a thinking cortex on top of a simpler

From *The New York Times Magazine,* September 10, 1967. Copyright © 1967 by The New York Times Company. Reprinted in revised form by permission.

brain. The idea of the evolution of *behavior,* however, has been slower to win support, for there is no "fossil behavior." From fossil bones, guesses can be made as to the ways that the bones were used, but how can anyone ever reliably know the origins of the habits of today's animals—or of our own?

Nevertheless, the evolution of behavior is now inspiring one of biology's hottest debates.

Darwin himself laid the groundwork for it when he wrote "The Expression of the Emotions in Man and Animals," and showed how closely alike the signs of emotion are. This book was largely ignored, at least in its implications, for the mechanical age had arrived and there was more interest in putting captive animals into pieces of apparatus, in testing their reflexes, their ability to find their way out of mazes, to count, and to discriminate between colors and forms—problems like these.

About 1950, however, a group calling themselves ethologists broke out of the laboratories, declaring that the most reliable facts about animal behavior are secured by watching animals in their natural habitats. From the discoveries made by these thoughtful observers, it soon became clear that we really don't know very much about how most animals lead their lives, about what animals do. Dr. William H. Thorpe of Cambridge University was one of the first to stride boldly onto the battlefield with the statement: "There is hardly any aspect of the behavior of animals which may not have some reference to problems in human behavior."

Some ethologists fell on that battlefield and went back to the laboratories. The ones who stayed in the field had to endure some ridicule; they were called Boy Scouts and taunted with the criticism that their work could not be a science since most of it was done without experimentation. Some of this obviously stung, for few ethologists are now simply trying to fill in the great gaps in our knowledge about the daily lives of wild animals. Work in the field must now include experimentation, and some ethologists are even confining the animals that they study in artificial environments which they call "semi-wild."

Meanwhile, the behavior of animals has fascinated the non-scientific public. Readers devour Joy Adamson's Elsa books, George Schaller's reports of his gorilla companions and those of Jane

Goodall about the chimpanzees with whom she and her husband live. An increasing number of popular films and television programs about animals whet this interest. And if orthodox biologists hold out against assuming any lines of descent in human behavior, from all sides laymen are asking what we can learn from living animals.

What about the relationship between the sexes? What about care of the young and their training, about the health of animals and how they maintain it, their feeding habits, how they relax and the ways in which they play? Above all, with war so great a threat in our lives, what about animal aggression?

This last has been the subject of two recent and readable books: "On Aggression," by Konrad Lorenz, and "The Territorial Imperative," by Robert Ardrey. Both authors declare that fighting is an instinct which demands expression in virtually all higher animals—and also in ourselves because, they claim, we have inherited this compulsion. Before examining their arguments, however, it is first necessary to define exactly what is meant by aggression.

Most laymen would think at once of predatory attacks on prey for food: the pursuit, the pounce, the kill. The biological definition, however, excludes this kind of slaughter because it involves no malice. A wolf bringing down an ill or aged caribou (a strong caribou can outrun a wolf) is no more angry than we are when we buy meat at the butcher's shop. He is merely hungry, as are other predators when prey is there and vulnerable.

Nor is there any true aggression, any malice, between members of different species going about their separate ways in the wilderness they share. They seem to recognize that each has different needs and perhaps, in their inarticulate way, they even recognize that other species have rights. On a path used by many or at a water hole or salt lick, the weaker and smaller animals await their turn, letting the stronger go first without argument.

Aggressiveness in its strict biological sense, and in the sense that Lorenz and Ardrey use the word, is expressed between two members *of the same species* when both want the same thing. With the great majority of animals, this same thing will be living space in which to raise the young of the year—an animal's homesite, also known as his territory.

Sometimes aggressiveness is aroused over possession of a desired female or over rank in a hierarchy. Biologists often call the space around a disputed female a territory. It moves when she moves and the male, going along, will not allow another male to approach within a certain well-understood distance.

Lorenz and Ardrey both tie their definition of aggressiveness in mankind to home territory. They call attention to properties marked with "No Trespassing" signs and—this is their ominous and essential theme—they extend the concept of farms or suburban lots to the nation, claiming that men fight to preserve or expand their national boundaries almost as involuntarily as they would their homes. They fight the soldiers of other nations because their remote animal ancestors once instinctively fought for nesting site, burrow, hunting range or the space which encircles a female.

Thus both Lorenz and Ardrey are convinced that war is an instinctive compulsion. Lorenz says that the most important function of animal aggression "is the spacing out of individuals of one species over the available habitat, in other words, the distribution of 'territories.'" He concludes: "There cannot be any doubt, in the opinion of any biologically minded scientist, that intra-specific aggression is, in man, just as much of a spontaneous instinctive drive as in most other higher vertebrates."

Ardrey, for his part, says: "If we defend the title to our land or the sovereignty of our country, we do it for reasons no different, no less innate, no less *ineradicable* than do the lower animals" (italics added). He also says: "All of us will give everything we are for a place of our own." And: "I believe man's innumerable territorial expressions are human responses to an imperative lying with equal force on mockingbirds and men."

Now, a widespread belief that human wars are instinctive, by which biologists mean inevitable, would of course tend to make them inevitable. Therefore it seems worthwhile to inquire whether aggression is universal in animals and just how insistent an urge it is. If aggression, as these authors insist, is a doom carried in human genes, we are predestined to wage wars and hopes for peace would seem to be slim. Lorenz does plead with some eloquence for an effort to replace competition for living space with competition in sports and other sublimations—but he already has made the urge to fight for territory seem so over-powering that the final impression left by

"On Aggression" leans toward the depressing view that fighting for territory is, in Ardrey's word, "ineradicable." That this is the lasting message gained from both books is shown by the comments of many reviewers and readers. The publicity for both, including pictures of viciously snarling animals, helps to promote this conviction.

It must be agreed that during mating seasons, at least, disputes over territorial boundary lines are prevalent. Spring, when most animal young are born and many conceived, is a time of much sparring for areas on which to raise them and find their food. But for some species, late summer and fall are the rutting season, and that is the time when the "territories" surrounding females are fought for.

In most cases, such aggressive behavior is related to reproductive needs. A territory, as space, can be as small as the single nesting tree defended by a woodpecker, or the range, nine miles or more in diameter, believed necessary to feed an average family of wolves.

To the creatures themselves, territory probably means home in the same way that home, for us, means more than house. To them the need may be temporary but it is not surprising that they instinctively fight for it.

But how universally and how desperately? The doom of eternal war would not seem so inescapable for us if some animals—indeed, if *any* of them—can escape the compulsion.

Caribou have no territories; neither do elephants. Sea otters don't. They copulate in the water and raise their young in fronds of seaweed. Whales are not likely to have individual homesites, although no one knows definitely. Lemmings live in villages, shallow excavations in the Arctic frost mounds, with several lemmings sleeping together in each nest until a gravid female is about to give birth, when she makes a nest of her own.

These could be called colonies. There are numerous animals in the temperate zone who have communal dwellings: gophers, prairie dogs, marmots. What goes on in their hidden worlds, at each stage of the annual cycle, is imperfectly known for most species. Some colonies defend the territory shared by all; it appears that others do not. Within the burrow it is customary for an individual family to defend its own unit.

What of cowbirds, which lay their eggs in other birds' nests and then are off to live on the backs of cattle (formerly bison), feeding on the parasites in their hosts' fur? It is amusing to speculate on whether individual cowbirds claim certain cows as their territory. It seems unlikely.

Among primates, most monkeys live in groups. In some there is a hierarchical social organization. Usually the dominant male has first choice when a female is in oestrus and discord often prevails. Other groups are sexually promiscuous and among them fighting often seems abhorrent. If youngsters are too aggressive, the adult males will separate them.

Howling monkeys claim possession of their communal areas but defend them generally with only vocal protests—as do gibbon families. When their screams fail to drive away intruders, gibbons may bite, but such occasions are rare.

The English ethologist J. H. Crook discussed the question of territory in The Listener, April 6, 1967. He explained the very flexible attitude of some birds and animals usually thought to defend territories. A territory "allows an individual to develop a close familiarity with a locality. This increases its food-finding efficiency and the speed of finding refuge from enemies." But some ducks that mate on their wintering grounds, or on migration, will accompany a new spouse to its homesite instead of returning to their own.

Species may change territories in response to local conditions. In drier years, certain marsh-dwelling weaver birds will disperse their nests over a large ground area; in wetter years, they may congregate in a large tree islanded in a flood pool. Harem groups of the gelada baboon wander independently in poor feeding years but "congregate in large herds of variable size under conditions of plenty. They have no territories, their disposition directly reflecting the local food availability."

Chimpanzees, says Dr. Crook, vary the size of their parties. As a rule individual and small groups wander over large home ranges and "territorial behavior appears to be absent." The facts are complex he says. "The dispersion pattern itself must depend largely on learning and tradition, and this is particularly so when we are talking about advanced mammals such as the monkeys. The sort of territory-holding present is more likely to be determined by the commodities for which the higher mammals compete than by any species characteristic directly determined by the genes. Thus in different ecologies, territorial systems will vary or even be absent altogether." These conclusions regarding the animals closest to us in the evolutionary scale seem very significant.

How unreliable are rigid definitions of territory was emphasized on Britain's BBC Third Program in August 1967 by Dr. Paul Layhausen, director of the Max Planck Institut at Wuppertal and described as "one of the world's foremost experts" on the subject of animal behavior. Territoriality is not just the static demarcation of an area, he said; it is part of a much more complex working out of a system of relationships in time as well as space—the very subtle and fluid pattern of "destiny tolerance." He continued: "There's much more to it still, of course: the difference between the ways in which mammals and birds 'survey' their territory . . . ; the interlacing of the routes by which animals go about their affairs, and the interrelation of the times at which they do things . . . Density tolerance is a matter of time as well as space."

One thinks of the fact that many bird parents will tolerate the trespassing of neighbors after their young are out of the nest: the time factor here seems more important than that of space.

Since most birds and animals which defend territories do limit this strongly emotional response to the reproductive season, a point to be considered is whether human beings, too, only feel animosity toward aliens while they are of the child-bearing age. Much depends on the individual, but that is the time, granted, when many homes are first established. If the most intense "territorial" feelings are typical of the young adults, how does it happen that most countries have to resort to conscription in order to raise their predominantly youthful military units? As is well known, those who enter the services voluntarily often do so to escape from conditions which seem stifling at the parental home. Others marry at about the same age and set up their own households. Some biologists, as an argument for territoriality, make much of the fact that animal young may be "driven out" in their second year. Observations in the wild suggest that few have to be driven. When they are ready to mate, they wish to form their own families and in order to do so, they leave.

Ardrey is not a biologist, as he himself explicitly and creditably states in his book. In reporting the work of professionals, he seems simply to have misjudged the emphasis that they put on territories and territorial aggression.

Lorenz, of course, is an ethologist of world repute, but his experience with animals is limited in a different way. He has done most of his research with tamed animals, such as geese induced by guard fences and food to live in a human environment, and with captive cichlid fishes in tanks. All creatures so confined have their aggressiveness heightened enormously.

As Lorenz himself explains, these two types of animals, fish and birds, are among those which demand "individual distance," meaning that they do not welcome, at any time, anywhere, the close approach of their con-specifics (the biological term for others of one's own species). Lorenz's fish and geese, disturbed by the enforced intimate association with their mates, have worked out rather elaborate rituals for "redirecting" their aggression—from mates to neighboring males. Since these are only symbolic attacks, the adjacent male seldom is injured, and the spouse, with his aggression now neutralized, returns to his mate triumphant.

Rituals *of the same sort* are not employed by our own class of animals, mammals, for mammals are "contact" species—that is, they seek and enjoy the touch of their own kind. This distinction between animals who want and those who do not want to be near their con-specifics is only mentioned briefly by Lorenz, but it is actually of the most basic importance.

Lorenz sets out in detail the observation that among all strongly aggressive animals there is a very powerful inhibition against killing con-specifics. Since they do, unavoidably, often annoy one another, however, various behavior patterns have become established to prevent fights with lethal consequences. The redirected aggression of fish and geese is one example; among mammals, a common mechanism is simply the flight of the weaker combatant. The victor does not pursue him; the fact that he gives in is satisfaction enough.

Serving the same purpose are many close-range gestures of submission or appeasement. Lorenz describes the well-known reaction of a defeated wolf. As soon as he recognizes that he will lose a fight, the wolf turns his head away, a movement that the victor immediately understands and accepts. When Lorenz described this wolf behavior in 1952 in "King Solomon's Ring," he spoke of it as the loser "offering his neck" to his opponent—moving evidence of good faith between wolves, inasmuch as the victor always withholds the final bite.

Since that time, Lorenz has more firmly become a "mechanist." In "On Aggression," he describes the loser's behavior as one of the "submissive or appeasing movements [which] have evolved from juvenile expression movements persisting into adulthood. This is not surprising to anyone who knows how strong the inhibition against attacking pups is in any normal dog." But however defined, the wolf ritual works; it prevents the killing of a con-specific.

Another form of ritualized, harmless fighting is the "tournament," such as the pushing contest between two ungulates (deer or other hoofed quadrupeds) during the rut. If they really wanted to kill each other, they would attack with their hoofs (as they do a predator). Instead they literally lock horns, each trying to make the other give way. As soon as one knows himself to be losing ground, he disengages his antlers, turns and runs, and the winner goes back to his females. It is a contest to see which is the stronger male—and the one, therefore, more likely to father superior fawns and, in those ungulate species in which the bulls defend the herd, more likely to prove a superior warden against predators.

Perhaps from their concentration on the subject, both Ardrey and Lorenz seem to have exaggerated impressions of the amount of con-specific aggression. At the start of Chapter II of "On Aggression," Lorenz writes: "What is the significance of all this fighting? In nature, fighting is such an ever-present process, its behavior mechanisms and weapons are so highly developed and have so obviously arisen under the selection pressure of a species-preserving function that it is our duty to ask this Darwinian question . . . Darwin's expression, 'the struggle for existence,' is sometimes erroneously interpreted as the struggle between different species. In reality, the struggle Darwin was thinking of . . . is the competition between near relatives."

When Lorenz writes of "all this fighting," and fighting as being "such an ever-present process" in nature, he is describing a wilderness that would not be recognized by those who, like myself, have lived there for years at a stretch.

On some mornings one finds blood on the snow where tracks of fox and hare collide, but that is evidence of predation, not the encounter of an animal with another of its own kind. Real aggression, usually reproductive in its origin and purpose, concerns the animals so briefly that most of the several dozen species I am familiar with spend far more than half their time—some of them as much as 11 months in the year—in casual or amiable association with their fellows.

Typical are black bears. After a rather perfunctory but successful courtship, a male returns to a drowsy life, the daytime often spent in a copse with four or five other males. They do, however, show animosity toward one of the off-shade bears that are a color phase of their own species. The forest rangers say that these rejected bears become neurotic. One charged me once, with small provocation. I escaped into my cabin but he stalked me for the next three weeks until, my exasperation boiling over, I attacked him, hurling rocks and language I hardly realized I knew. He left for good—I hope with no new psychological trauma.

Both Lorenz and Ardrey distinguish too briefly between offensive and defensive fighting. Is one who defends his territory "aggressive?" If not, if only an invader is properly so described, how many do thus intrude? Extremely few, except in captivity. Among wolves, one who comes into the territory of another's family may be seeking companionship (a "lone wolf" is usually an orphan). According to most observers, he is not attacked; he is simply threatened and he leaves—and is not pursued to the border. Even the young ungulate bull or buck does not often boldly challenge an older, stronger male. He tries to steal a female, and when he encounters the leader's anger, at once retires to a safer distance.

Those who describe the wilderness from a domestic garden like Darwin's or Lorenz's fenced enclosure and laboratory or Ardrey's library, tend to put the emphasis on a few, dramatic animals like rats, wolves and lions.

Rats are contact species, and to explain some fights he saw among rats, Lorenz suggests that they were not personal confrontations, that rat clans tend to kill all outsiders. Such group aggressiveness would seem especially ominous because of the possible analogy with mankind's national wars. But here, as with geese and fish, Lorenz is presenting evidence provided by captives, and captives held in conditions so unsatisfactory as to stimulate fighting.

As Lorenz describes them: "Steiniger put brown rats from different localities into a large enclosure which provided them with completely natural living conditions. At first the individual animals seemed afraid of each other; they were not in an aggressive mood, but they bit each other if they met by chance, particularly if two were driven towards each other along one side of the enclosure, so that they collided at speed." (Most biologists, incidentally, would not call the conditions provided by any enclosure as "completely natural"—especially not if it were so small that individuals collided when racing along the fence.)

Steiniger's rats soon began to attack one another and fought until all but one pair were killed. The descendants of that pair formed a clan, which subsequently slaughtered every strange rat introduced into the habitat.

During the same years that this study was being conducted, John B. Calhoun in Baltimore was also investigating the behavior of rats. There were 15 rats in F. Steiniger's original population; 14 in Calhoun's—also strangers to one another. But Calhoun's enclosure was *16 times* larger than Steiniger's and more favorable in other ways: "harborages" were provided for rats pursued by hostile associates (such refuges would probably exist in the wild), and all Calhoun's rats were identified by markings.

For 27 months, from a tower in the center of the large area, the movements of all the individual rats were recorded. After a few fights while getting acquainted, they separated into two clans, neither of which tried to eliminate the other. There was a good deal of crossing back and forth unchallenged—so often by some individuals that they were dubbed messengers.

Steiniger has also observed rat clans on a small island in the North Sea. They were rather belligerent in a neutral no-man's-land. But isn't it possible that these rat populations were outgrowing the available living area? The crowdedness of many communities is surely one cause for the dangerous degree of aggressiveness now existing throughout the world. War and the population explosion: these influences must be related—to what extent would seem to be a most promising study of man's belligerent motives. But as for clan-aggressiveness, *per se,* many of us believe that this cannot be identified with any certainty as an evolutionary source of human wars.

Other than rats, wolves, and lions, there is a vast kingdom of little lives absorbed in the business of living. When Lorenz says that "fighting is an ever-present process" in nature, he must be forgetting all the moles, hedgehogs, raccoons, opossums, woodchucks, otters, chipmunks, squirrels of several kinds, rabbits, lemmings, moles, muskrats and beavers—not "eager," as a leisure generation of human beings has facetiously called them, but terribly earnest about creating one of the most complex (and needed) animal "estates" on earth. It is usual for them to respect one another's ownership of these properties.

Lorenz says that only the most aggressive creatures ever form permanent pairs, but beavers mate for life. And although their gnawing teeth would serve as very effective weapons, I have never known any occasion when they were so used against con-specifics. In their cleverly built houses, behind the dams and network of canals they have constructed, they live in notable harmony with one another and with the muskrats, for whom they provide ponds and who may be welcomed into beaver houses—as badgers will receive, and make friends with, coyotes and foxes.

How would such animals have *time* for continual fighting? What the absent biologists do not seem to realize is that a wilderness is a community of workers. Simply finding enough to eat every day is a chancy and tiring task. Think of the vast bulk of a whale to be nourished and the problems of providing for a family of wolves (averaging 12).

One has a mental picture of field mice running around everywhere in sufficient numbers to sustain the predators, but examination of some coyotes' stomach contents showed that, for days, they had eaten nothing but small amounts of berries, carrion, garbage and old scraps of leather.

It may be a surprise to know that many animals also spend a great deal of time keeping themselves clean and, if possible, free of parasites. Primates groom one another for hours every day. One year, one of the small pretty deer-mice came in to share my cabin, and sometimes I wished she would stop washing her fur; she did it so incessantly it was tiring to watch. (When I bathed, sponging water over myself from the basin in which I stood, she always took up a position in front of me and went through her own bathing routine. I used to wonder whether she sensed the analogy. I don't think she did but I enjoyed asking the question.)

Such mammals as these, in rising strata of complexity—these are our ancestors, more recent than the primitive, sexually antagonistic fish and geese. Many mammals have never even developed rituals to prevent the death of con-specifics, because they don't need them. Except when attacked by a predator, they quite simply do not fight.

Our immediate forebears, the apes, seem to have reached something like a summit in nonaggressiveness, since they do not fight either—not as individuals or as clans. Lorenz suggests that they do not attack their associates because they do not have such effective weapons as the teeth of wolves or the paws of lions, but would not the arm of a full-grown male gorilla be as strong as a lion's paw?

We do not know which mammals were the nearest ancestors of primates, but there are sufficient numbers of nonaggressive creatures living today to suggest that co-operation was becoming the habit of evolving mammals even before the primates developed. What, therefore, has happened? Man obviously is an aggressive animal. We have lost both the peacefulness and the inhibition against killing others of our own kind. Is there an explanation?

As Lorenz points out, aggressiveness can be taught. It is also intensified when it is exercised (and atrophies when it is not). When men began to settle in communities, they learned the irritations of being crowded. By then they had probably learned the use of weapons, originally for the purpose of killing game. And since they had already acquired at least a rudimentary speech, they could absorb from one another, and preach, animosity. With words, they could incite hatred against neighboring tribes. A leader, coveting power or property, could, with propaganda, instill in his subjects admiration for warlike attitudes.

Perhaps that is the way—culturally rather than genetically—that human aggressiveness arose. As for sadism, something no animal displays, it is my belief that the trait is psychotic. (In the case of cats' treatment of mice, research indicates that it is pure play—though useful as practice of hunting skills. The cat probably does not realize that it is torturing the mice.)

Nothing could more effectively prolong man's fighting behavior than a belief that aggression is in our genes. An unwelcome cultural inheritance can be eradicated fairly quickly and easily, but the incentive to do it is lacking while people believe that aggression is innate and instinctive with us, as both Ardrey and Lorenz declare.

More than 100 years ago, the philosopher William Whewell wrote: "There is a mask of theory over the whole face of nature." Anyone writing about the wilderness has a great responsibility not to accept too readily a belief that the mask is nature's true face. In a chaotic and perfidious world, nature is all we have that is infallibly real.

If writers assert their own, unproven hypotheses as the truth, civilized people, so isolated from the wilderness that they cannot recognize a fallacy when they hear one, will be deprived in their one lifeline of what may be felt intuitively as sane and good. Then, even the intuition will be lost—what is there left for anybody but madness?

J. P. SCOTT

That Old-Time Aggression

The control of destructive violence between individuals and nations is one of the major practical problems of our times. Its consequences are so great that it deserves a major scientific effort directed toward its solution, and its causes are so many and so various that scientists from almost every discipline, from mathematics through physiology and biological sciences to the social sciences, have something to contribute. *On Aggression* is such a contribution, written by the distinguished European ethologist Konrad Lorenz.

It is a beautifully written and translated book, and follows a line of argument which almost anyone can understand. Lorenz apparently began it as a reaction against Freud's interpretation of aggression as an impulse of destruction directed both toward others and toward oneself. He points out that fighting behavior in the animal kingdom had evolved in many different ways and usually serves some useful function, such as the dispersal of animals throughout their living space and the division of land into breeding territories so that adequate food is available for the young. And he describes human aggressive impulses as probably having had some such constructive function in primitive man. Aggression is therefore not necessarily an·evil, but is evil because it has been distorted from its original function.

No modern student of the evolution of animal behavior would

From *The Nation*, January 9, 1967, pp. 53–54. Reprinted by permission.

quarrel with this viewpoint, and this is a major contribution to the understanding of aggressive behavior in animal societies.

Nevertheless, this is a disappointing book, both from a scientific and a practical point of view. Lorenz explains aggressive behavior on the basis of instinct, an idea which was popular around the turn of the century, and his solution for the problem, sublimation, was presented with equal eloquence and greater practicality by William James in his essay on "The Moral Equivalent of War," in 1910.

To understand why a modern biologist would publish a book which leaves out of consideration most of the scientific discoveries of the past 50 years requires some knowledge of Lorenz. He is a very intelligent person who picks up ideas quickly and who has a great deal of verbal and written fluency. He also has the ability to make friends quickly and to communicate a sense of excitement, and by these personal qualities he has been able to inspire a great many people to enter the field of animal behavior, or ethology, as it is sometimes called. He is also kindly and humanitarian, and this comes through in both his personal contacts and his writings.

At the same time he is a very narrow specialist, who primarily knows the behavior of birds, and particularly that of ducks and geese, on which his book has an excellent chapter. He evidently reads very little other than material which is directly related to his own specialty. Consequently, when he began observing the behavior of birds from the viewpoint of native behavior, or instinct, he went back to the writings of other students of bird life, Wallace Craig and Whitman, for his theoretical concepts. Lorenz quotes articles published in 1918, and most of the ideas in them had been worked out years before. This was before modern geneticists had begun to work out the consequences of the facts of Mendelian genetics in relation to evolution, and it was also before the publication of much of the modern work on the physiology of the emotions and appetites. These ideas of instinct are thus pre-Mendelian and pre-physiological, and in this day and age such a classical theory of instinct forms a very incomplete and inadequate explanation of behavior.

One of the major points in Lorenz's theory is the spontaneity of aggression. To him, this is self-evident. But for a physiologist there must be a demonstration of chemical and physical changes within the body which would lead to such "spontaneous" aggressive behavior. A series of these changes are well known in the case of hunger, where the cells use up blood sugar, which in turn stimulates certain centers of the brain which then cause hunger contractions in the stomach, thus making one more ready to eat. The situation with respect to the emotion of anger is quite different. Beginning with the studies of the American physiologist Walter B. Cannon, whose book *Bodily Changes in Pain, Hunger, Fear, and Rage* was published in 1929, it has been shown that the emotion of anger originates in one portion of the brain, the hypothalamus, and stimulating this area with electrodes in an animal such as a cat will produce reactions very similar to anger. Without such stimulation the animal is quiet. Evidence obtained from the removal of parts of the brain shows that certain other areas have a stimulating effect on anger, and that these are balanced by other portions which inhibit it. Stimulation from the outside, such as the pain of a blow, will upset the balance and cause the emotion of anger. Thus we have a mechanism which prolongs and magnifies the effects of external stimulation but no mechanism for building up the first stimulation from within. There is no internal change corresponding to the change in blood sugar which results in hunger. In short, the physiological evidence is against Lorenz's notion of the spontaneity of aggression, and indeed, it is difficult to see how such a mechanism for spontaneity could have evolved. Fighting is an emergency reaction, and it is hard to imagine how natural selection would lead to the development of a mechanism of continuous internal accumulation of energy which would unnecessarily put an animal into danger.

This may appear to be a fine technical point, but it has one important consequence. If Lorenz is right, then man can never lead a happy, peaceful existence, but must continually be sublimating the spontaneous "drive" which accumulates within him. If the physiologists are correct, then it is theoretically possible for man to lead a happy and peaceful existence provided he is not continually stimulated to violence. Sublimation will have its uses, because in any practical situation there will always be some accidental stimulation toward violence, but it is only one of the many techniques provided by modern scientific knowledge for the control of aggression.

As for other major causes of aggression, such as heredity and training, Lorenz simply leaves them out. Heredity has major effects upon the development of aggressiveness, both between animal species and between individuals of the same kind. Training has equally important effects on the higher animals. We know that through appropriate training methods, an animal like a mouse can be converted into an individual which will attack females and even infant mice, something which mice normally never do. A male mouse, by other methods, can be trained to be completely peaceful. Lorenz has also completely missed (and this may be because of his lack of acquaintance with research done on mammals) one of the major recent findings of research on animal behavior. Social organization is not something which is born into an animal, but something which is developed, and if social organization is disturbed, harmless or even beneficial aggressive behavior can be transformed into destructive violence. Thus the violent baboons in the London Zoo studied by Zuckerman were a group of individuals strange to each other and hence a disorganized society. The undisturbed societies of baboons studied by Washburn and DeVore on the South African plains present an entirely different picture. Fighting is present but controlled by a dominance order, and is chiefly directed against predators, and one sees the baboons risking their lives for the benefit of a group. Thus a baboon, in common with many other mammals, has the capacity to develop destructive violence under conditions of social disorganization, whereas under the proper conditions of social organization he has the capacity to develop peaceful and cooperative behavior, to direct fighting into useful channels, and to act in a manner which might well be described as altruistic. One wonders whether the same might not be said of man.

There is an element in human behavior, however, which goes beyond this simple formulation. Man is a tool user, and one of the tools that men have discovered is that they can organize themselves into groups for the purpose of destruction and violence, and that such trained groups will overcome any individual or untrained group. This is one of the major causes of warfare—its usefulness or apparent usefulness for attaining certain ends—and it presents a problem which can only be solved on the level of human social organization.

In brief, fighting is a complex phenomenon, taking many forms, and is stimulated and controlled by many different factors. Any "single factor" explanation, such as that of instinct, is necessarily incomplete. To give Lorenz proper credit, he would probably write a different book if he were to write it today, as in a more recent volume he has begun to incorporate the phenomenon of learning into his theories of the evolution of behavior.

The Territorial Imperative is a very different kind of a book, although Konrad Lorenz is one of Ardrey's heroes. Briefly stated, Ardrey's thesis, carried over from his earlier book, *African Genesis,* is that human aggression has an even simpler basis than that postulated by Lorenz, namely "man's instinct for territoriality." This is presented so naïvely that even an unscientific reader is not likely to take the book seriously, and Ardrey himself realizes that the evidence from field studies of primates goes against his ideas.

Ardrey's book can also be better understood in terms of the history of its author. Ardrey began his career as a dramatist, with little or no formal training in science. In a sentence, *Territorial Imperative* is good theater and third-rate science reporting, full of entertainment and wild analogies.

In the early 1940's I published a scientific paper demonstrating that there were inherited differences between the fighting capacities of two pure strains of mice. Males of the gray strain were irritable and quick to start a fight, whereas those of the black strain were slow to start, but once the fighting began they almost always won over the grays. After its publication, I was interviewed by a newspaper reporter who wanted me to say that this situation was "just like ourselves and the Germans." It took some minutes before I was able to persuade him that the resemblance was purely superficial, that mice are not just like people, and that the differences between the behavior of Germans and ourselves were mostly due to culture, rather than to any profound biological difference.

This unsophisticated level of science reporting has become much rarer than it used to be, but it has survived in full strength in Ardrey's book. To him, a band of lemurs in Madagascar is just like a modern human nation.

Ardrey has read widely in the scientific literature on territoriality, but his ideas, if not always as wildly unsophisticated as my reporter's, are equally uncritical. He has written these down as they come to him, and the result is a sort of intellectual pizza pie, with tasty tidbits of information embedded in a mass of partially baked ideas.

This is too bad, because a good popular account of territoriality could be written. The facts are that territoriality occurs only in the higher animals such as the vertebrates and arthropods and even there in a very spotty fashion. In primates, our closest biological relatives, there are many cases of species which have no real territories. To take one of the more aggressive primates as an example, rhesus monkeys live in a core area and as a group wander out into a more extended range which overlaps with that of other groups by as much as 80 per cent. There are dominant and subordinate groups, and ordinarily the subordinate groups avoid contact. If they meet unexpectedly, the dominant group will attack, no matter where the contact takes place. There is plenty of fighting, but none of it is related to territory. Baboon groups live in similar overlapping home ranges, and DeVore and Hall never saw a group defend a territorial boundary. Unlike the rhesus, groups tolerate each other, and there are few conflicts even when groups come into close contact around water holes. On the other hand, there are some recently described primate groups that apparently defend rather precise territorial boundaries just as some birds do.

We have no knowledge whatever about the territorial behavior of pre-cultural man, and even if we did there has been ample opportunity for genetic change to have taken place within the past several hundred thousand years. We will have to make our judgments on territoriality in human beings on the basis of modern man himself, and here the anthropologists tell us that the importance of territoriality and private property varies enormously between different cultures. To present an extreme example, in none of the Eskimo societies except the Aleut was there any such thing as the defense of "territory," even though the introduction of a strange group into a hunting area might mean starvation and death for the original inhabitants. Other societies have believed that they held rights to certain animals or plants in a territory, but not to others; or they have believed that while the tribe as a whole held rights to a territory, no individual or individual family could claim special rights to any particular piece of ground. In short, there is no evidence that territoriality is or is not a biologically determined universal condition in modern man, but a great deal of evidence of important cultural differences. There *may* be some biological basis for territorial behavior in people, but it is equally possible that it is a human cultural invention.

Will *The Territorial Imperative* have a bad effect? It reminds me of another book that I read when I was fifteen—Albert Edward Wiggam's *The Fruit of the Family Tree*. This book, now happily forgotten, was an attempt to apply what was then known about the science of animal breeding to human affairs. It was the author's simple thesis that all human ills were caused by bad heredity, and that if we were to breed human beings with the same care that we did animals all the world's problems could be solved. To an unsophisticated fifteen-year-old it seemed that if heredity was this important someone would study heredity and behavior seriously and apply the knowledge accordingly. I went ahead to specialize in the science of genetics and, of course, the more I learned about it the more it became obvious that there were other important factors that determined behavior and that heredity was only one of the many causes operating within the extraordinarily complex systems which comprise animal and human behavior.

Ardrey's book may inspire present-day fifteen-year-olds to go and learn more about the science of animal and human behavior and the causes of destructive violence. If so, it will have had a good effect. Unfortunately, fifteen-year-olds have no monopoly on lack of sophistication, and unsophisticated adults sometimes get into positions of power. Simple-minded ideas similar to those of Wiggam concerning racial improvement led Hitler and his friends to try to eliminate one whole section of the human race. I doubt if Ardrey's book has any such serious implication as this, but the erroneous notion that fighting over the possession of land is a powerful, inevitable, and uncontrollable instinct might well lead to the conclusion that war is inevitable and therefore a nation must attack first and fight best in order to survive and prosper. It is to be hoped that the persons in power in our society are too sophisticated to fall for any such adolescent interpretation of world affairs, but history will, as usual, have the last word. Meanwhile, we can say that

Ardrey's thesis is an over-simplified and therefore largely erroneous answer to an extraordinarily complex problem.

The popularization of scientific information in our society is a very important task, as the ultimate usefulness of science depends upon its getting into the minds of as many people as possible. That this can be done in both a readable and scientifically authentic way is demonstrated by such books as Amram Scheinfeld's *You and Heredity*. Trained only as a writer, Scheinfeld set out to present the science of genetics to the general public. However, he worked with a geneticist until he thoroughly understood the material himself, and when he had written the book he submitted it to scientists for criticism. Originally published in 1939, this book became an immediate popular success. As the years went by, Scheinfeld published new editions as the science of genetics changed and developed, and his latest book, under the title of *Your Heredity and Environment* (Lippincott, 1965), is a major resource for any one who wishes to become informed on the science of genetics. In contrast, the reader who wishes to know about territoriality may be attracted by the title of Ardrey's book, but what he will get will be entertainment. For authentic information he will have to go to original sources.

Instinct and Aggression

Dr. Lorenz, Director of the Max Planck Institute for Behavioral Physiology in Germany and author of works on animal behavior, has written two new books on important subjects. In *Evolution and Modification of Behavior* (Chicago, 1965) he discusses his theory of animal behavior; in *On Aggression* (a translation of his book *Das Sogennante Böse,* Vienna, 1963) he applies this theory to a problem in social behavior. Both books are based on dubious assumptions.

Aggression is defined as "The fighting instinct in beast and man which is directed against members of the same species." The thesis for man and beast alike is: Aggressive instincts dominate behavior unless curbed. The importance of this point for man is stressed: Someone from another planet, " . . . looking upon man as he is today, in his hand the atom bomb, the product of his intelligence, in his heart the aggression drive, inherited from his anthropoid ancestors, which this same intelligence cannot control, would not predict long life for the species."

The concept of instinctual aggression is of course not new. That such an instinct was paramount in natural selection is an idea Lorenz shares with Herbert Spencer (first to speak of "survival of the fittest") who featured aggression instinct as a major factor in man's evolution, and with Freud. Lorenz finds aggression and

From *Natural History,* December 1966. Reprinted by permission. New material added by author, 1968.

fighting common in lower animals and considers them potent in the evolution of all animals.

On Aggression begins with vivid accounts of observations of strikingly colored coral-reef fishes in tanks and in the sea. Cases are described in which each observed territory-holder, excited by an invader of his own species, attacks and drives off the trespasser.

Although the results of these studies on coral-reef fishes are engagingly presented, and open the statement of evidence in which they are featured, the reader has no means by which to appraise their reliability. The experiments with coral-reef fishes in laboratory tanks were carried out with subjects that were not always in good condition and—as an equally serious drawback—were not so designed as to control crowding as a factor in influencing the behavior described. The author's observations on reactions of these fishes in the sea are eloquently reported; unfortunately, there is no mention of the observational checks and balances that are indispensable to bring recollections of free observations out of the area of subjective impression and into the area of reliability. Hence the conclusions drawn are open to question.

Territorial-defense fighting, common in lower vertebrates, birds and mammals, is then discussed as crucial in natural selection in its role as a basis for food-getting, mating, rearing young, and other behavior promoting species survival. In lower animals, instinctive aggression is viewed as working well; in man, however, the author expresses concern that it has been getting out of hand.

Mechanisms that inhibit fighting, Lorenz holds, are essential to survival in lower animals and man alike. Chief among these are ritualistic displays in which aggressors are warded off with little or no physical contact. In man, however, the inhibitory controls imposed on aggression both through natural selection and through cultural processes may fail in the split-second emergencies created by modern weaponry and related bellicose patterns. Man is " . . . the only being capable of dedicating himself to the highest moral and ethical values . . . " but " . . . whose animal properties bring with them the danger that he will kill his brother, convinced that he is doing so in the interests of these very same high values. *Ecce homo!" Behold man!*—that is, as Lorenz sees him.

Lorenz shares this sombre view with Freud, who also saw conflict and war as inevitable, violent expressions of irresponsible human aggressive instincts. Lorenz, like Freud, considers the social bond and related influences inadequate to inhibit man's dominantly aggressive biological nature in the modern world.

In his chapter, "Avowal of Optimism," Lorenz sugggests that man, under the described threat, must find methods for ritualizing and channelizing instinctive aggressions, must encourage people of differing ideologies and races to get acquainted, must direct "the militant enthusiasms" of youth toward "genuine causes that are worth serving in the modern world," and must improve his understanding of behavioral mechanisms fundamental to aggression, the better to control them. Finally, he must use his resources of humor and of knowledge to these ends. These suggestions, although helpful, seem to reveal an aspect of Freudian sublimation; that is, of making the best of a bad deal.

A different picture of man, however, based on current scientific theory and methodology, is at odds with Lorenz's outdated negative view. Results of research on human group behavior emphasize man's great social potentials arising from his developmental plasticity and his versatility for constructive behavior. At the same time, evidence on the origins of *asocial* behavior suggests that hypotheses in which instinctual aggression is offered to explain the rise of wars are tangential and naïve.

The question is not whether results from investigations of behavior in lower animals are applicable to man, but whether the application is as simple a matter as Lorenz's procedures imply. Responsible scientists must carry out their research on behavior within the broadest perspective and evaluate evidence in terms of the most valid theory possible. Evidence on individual differences, on the conditions of development, and on the state of the population must be featured, for these surely were all crucial in the natural selective background of every animal. The results of research must be presented in comprehensive reports open to searching analysis; not in descriptive, subjective terms as Lorenz does in this book.

The significance Lorenz gives his results is too great to justify his non-experimental, anecdotal treatment of the subject. An appropriately broad, systematic presentation of the behavioral facts would have aided readers to understand, for example, how very differently individual fish may have responded according to the conditions (e.g., stressful crowding in aquaria), and how results from observations of animals in confinement actually compared with the behavior of these same animals under natural conditions.

Studying social phenomena and other behavior under natural conditions is extremely important, and the ethological approach inspired by Lorenz and Tinbergen has aided such work, which ideally goes hand in hand with laboratory research. The field of behavioral development is highly controversial, however, in ways that do not emerge clearly in . . . *Behavior*. Lorenz's critics dispute neither his emphasis on " . . . the great fact of adaptiveness in behavior . . . ," as he implies, nor on correlations between genotypes (empirically described species genetics) and phenotypes (individual patterns developed). Rather, they reject much of his evidence as partial and unreliable, and question on these and other grounds the assumptions he applies dogmatically to these problems.

It is not clear from . . . *Behavior* whether or not science will be aided by Lorenz's terms, "phyletic information" and "individually acquired information," which he confuses consistently with reality. These concepts, notwithstanding the impressive cybernetic aura he gives them and the polemical deftness with which he uses them in explanatory roles, do not differ much from their traditional synonyms, "nature" and "nurture," respectively.

Space precludes discussing here the obfuscations raised in . . . *Behavior* for readers who try to judge the theoretical issues involved in the book. Lorenz admits that the terms "innate" and "learned" used (by "earlier ethologists") to denote mutually exclusive agencies, are fallacious. But at the same time, in speaking of "information" that is either "phyletically acquired" or "individually acquired," he revives the fallacious dichotomy by using the word *information* in two different senses. He repeats his assertion of some years ago that others (whose evidence and ideas he evades) offered "learning in the egg and *in utero*" to explain ontogenesis, although he should know *by now* that this gambit is both an untrue statement and a misrepresentation of important evidence. But Lorenz's positivism often leads him to exclude evidence on behavioral development that is at odds with his assumptions.

Two related devices stand out in the book. One is the term "innate school-marm" for hypothetical genetic agencies presumed to determine what the animal is to learn as it develops. Another is the "deprivation experiment," formerly the "isolation experiment," offered here as *the* method for determining what is innate. The author directs these ideas at the separation of innate and learned elements in behavior with a faith in their soundness hardly justified by available evidence or comprehensive theory. His implication that the genes rigidly "program" the animal's learning is opposed by the results of many experiments, also by evidence from animal training that, under appropriate developmental conditions, animals do many things that species mates never do ordinarily. The deprivation experiment, as he terms it now, is better called the change-of-environment test, as it is widely used to study behavioral differences in young animals raised under conditions other than those presumed to be natural for them. Believing that " . . . it can only tell us directly what is not learned," the author must assume that he knows beforehand the developmental significances of these "natural" conditions. This, however, is precisely the problem needing investigation. Actually, this method is only one part of the behavior investigator's repertoire, now widely used in developmental research of much wider scope than is considered in . . . *Behavior*.

Lorenz's argument is built from the assumption that patterns such as aggression are seated specifically in the genes. It is a long way from the genes to behavior, however, and the books under review do not light the way. This key assumption is not only unsupported; it is also denied by a sizable weight of evidence. As is well known, the frequency and nature of aggressive behavior varies among members of both inter-species and intra-species groups raised together under conditions favorable to one or to another pattern of behavioral development.

Lorenz seems interested neither in the study of individual differences nor in phyletic comparisons in behavioral development; yet these problems are vital to understanding how aggression, for example, arises and varies in widely different types of animals. The question of why, when two fish react to invasions of their territory, one flees whereas the other attacks, or why some people generally are peaceable whereas others are quarrelsome, is not easy. Neither is it the same question for fish and for people. All available methods (including "deprivation tests") must be used for studying such differences in function and in behavior throughout development.

The more scientists study behavioral development and the more they study its properties through the animal series, the less likely are they to follow Lorenz's oversimplified formula which he applies uncritically to all integrative levels. As an example, in certain animals on what I have called the "biosocial level," chemical secretions, according to concentrations, attract or repel species mates, thereby dominating behavior. Ants, bees, and wasps offer good examples of biological processes controlling behavior directly. But insects are not people. On the "psychosocial level," in contrast, structural and physiological factors contribute indirectly to behavior and differently according to the conditions of individual development. In man, adrenalin, a neurosecretory excitatory substance, can arouse fighting, loving, poetizing, preaching, singing or panic according to the individual's background and his current situation. The assumptions underlying the theory expounded in these books are sufficiently open to question for lower animals; their free extrapolation to man is therefore quite doubtful.

It is as heavy a responsibility to inform mankind about aggressive tendencies assumed to be present on an inborn basis as about "original sin"—and this Lorenz admits in effect. A corollary risk is advising societies to base their programs of social training on attempts to inhibit *hypothetical* innate aggressions, instead of continuing positive measures for socially constructive behavior. Major aggressions of history, including Hitler's, may be explained superficially by the easy devices of instinct theory, or studied systematically with evidence known to historians and scientists.

Don't Say "Boo" to a Goose

As a mine of scientific-sounding misinformation Mr. Robert Ardrey would be hard to beat, but his application of the techniques of TV drama writing to the more musty corners of academic orthodoxy certainly livens things up. Looking up a well-known and easily accessible reference acquires the excitement of a James Bond spy story: "I at last found a copy in the guarded library of today's Royal Anthropological Institute in Bedford Square." Everything is black and white. Conventional professional scientists with whom Ardrey disagrees become criminal conspirators worthy only of the crudest ridicule; for his friends, the ethologists, no praise can be too high: "When Konrad Lorenz's book appears in Britain and America" it will "take its place among the landmarks of our thought." It has now appeared and it is no landmark, but it is modest and wise, while Ardrey's version is only noisy and foolish. The two books have a common central theme—the function of innate aggression in man and other animals. Ardrey concentrates on what ethologists call "territoriality," that is the drive to defend property aggressively, and he operates with very crude nineteenth-century ideas about how the evolutionary process works—"the survival of the fittest"—"Nature red in tooth and claw" and all that. Lorenz, on the other hand, is concerned to show that animal aggression is only a "so-called evil" and that its adaptive consequences are advantageous or at least neutral. Fighting between members of the same species helps to secure an even distribution of the species over its inhabitable area, and "aggression" has been responsible for all the more gorgeously dramatic, but inefficient, products of evolution, such as the Bird of Paradise and the Argus Pheasant. On which point Heinroth has remarked: "Next to the wings of the Argus Pheasant, the hectic life of western civilized man is the most stupid product of intraspecific selection"! For Lorenz, an even more striking virtue of aggression lies in its negation and control. Nature has had to ensure that aggressive animals shall not exterminate themselves by mutual slaughter. Thus behavior which signifies aggressive hostility towards enemies comes to be modified into a "ritualized" form which signals love and amity between friends. If we take fish and birds as our models, then the basic morality which allows a man to love his wife and respect his neighbor's property has the same instinctive source as the basic immorality which leads to war and destruction.

But can we take fish and birds as our models? In observing how animals behave we can only record what they do and the circumstances in which they do it; we know nothing about their feelings and motives. But when we discuss human behavior our objectivity is fogged by subjective private experience. It may be perfectly sensible to describe the action of a baboon in baring its teeth towards an opponent as "an aggressive gesture." For the Chinese Government to authorize the test firing of a nuclear rocket may also be properly described as "an aggressive gesture." But to argue that the two behaviors are comparable in anything except a purely metaphorical sense is just nonsense. Yet this is precisely what both our authors are up to all the time. They want to imply that the political policies of modern states are in some sense predetermined by the genetic constitution of *Homo sapiens*. Ardrey argues quite explicitly that Indian-Chinese border disputes are analogous to squabbles between two varieties of geese sharing the same pool! This is just word-play, and as with any other verbal conjuring trick it can be played in several different ways. Despite Ardrey's praise for Lorenz, the conclusions of the two books are diametrically opposed. Lorenz finds room for limited Christian-Confucian optimism—future salvation will be found in a specific human capacity "to love all our human brothers indiscriminately," Ardrey offers us only a crude Hobbesian war of all against all—"we are predators, of course, and from time to time we shall go out looting and raping and raising general havoc." Ardrey explicitly compares man's "killing propensity" to that of a wolf (p. 340); this precisely is what Lorenz repudiates:

> A wolf can rip the jugular vein of another with a single bite. There would be no more wolves if reliable inhibitions did not prevent such actions. Neither a dove nor a hare nor even a chimpanzee is able to kill its own kind with a single peck or bite. . . animals with relatively poor defense weapons have a correspondingly greater ability to escape quickly, even from specially armed predators who are more efficient in chasing, catching and killing than even the strongest of their own species. (*On Aggression*, 1966, p. 240)

> [The statement that man has a carnivorous mentality] confuses the concepts of the carnivore and the cannibal, which are, to a very large extent, mutually exclusive. One can only deplore the fact that man has definitely not got a carnivorous mentality! All his trouble arises from his being a basically harmless, omnivorous creature, lacking weapons with which to kill big prey, and, therefore, also devoid of the built-in safety devices which prevent "professional" carnivores from abusing their killing power to destroy fellow members of their own species. A lion or a wolf may, on extremely rare occasions, kill another by one angry stroke, but . . . all heavily armed carnivores possess sufficiently reliable inhibitions which prevent the self-destruction of the species. (p. 241)

Although every schoolboy will tell you that it was Charles Darwin who first conceived the notion that Man might be descended from an ape and that he devised this heresy some time around 1859, the truth is that Man's relationship to other animals has been a matter of fascinated conjecture for most of mankind throughout most of human history: The foster-mother of Romulus was a wolf, Helen of Troy was fathered by a swan. More recently the eighteenth-century Neapolitan, Giambattista Vico, imagined the ancestors of modern men to be speechless giants having the attributes of a gorilla; the slightly younger J. J. Rousseau argued that anthropoid apes are real human beings existing in a state of nature. But although Darwin's heresy had long been a commonplace, we are still reluctant to admit its implications. Men indeed are animals, but surely they are more than that? And having imagined that this distinction is clear-cut, we go on to persuade ourselves that it is the non-animal, human, part of ourselves which is by far the most important. In the eighteenth century this distinction was embodied in the word *Reason*. Man possessed Reason, animals did not. The late nineteenth century substituted a more complex idea—*Culture*. The lives of mere animals, it was said, are determined by inherited characteristics, "instincts"; the lives of human beings on the other hand, are determined by habits transmitted by learning within a social context. Human beings are sharply distinguished from all other animals by their sophisticated powers of communication, by consciousness of personal identity, and by their awareness of property rights over things and persons and places. We flatter ourselves. We now know that though rats have not yet got around to nuclear warfare or telemetry, they can learn how to recognize poisoned food *and* pass on this information to their more ignorant acquaintances, and if we systematically investigate just how this might be possible, the classic dichotomy between *instinct* and *culture* becomes very blurred indeed. Certainly we are much more clever than the rats and the possession of spoken language makes a hell of a difference, but just how much difference?

This, essentially, is what these two books are about. Both are attempts to provide "popular," boiled-down versions of the implications of ethology (the study of animal behavior) for the human understanding of human beings. This is tricky country, and Lorenz's naiveté is often quite as misleading as Ardrey's downright error. Ethologists concern themselves with the competition for survival between whole animal species, and they have been particularly ingenious in showing how inbred peculiarities of appearance and behavior are adaptively advantageous in the age-long sequence of genetic evolution. But when ethologists start talking about Man they are inclined to write as if "a whole culture" was somehow comparable to "a whole species," which is really just nonsense. If a *species* "dies out" the individuals concerned cease to exist; if a *culture* "dies out" it may mean no more than that Cowboys and Indians have learned to drive Cadillacs. At one point Lorenz, growing sentimental about the evolutionary advantages of cultural norms, writes:

> The studies of the ethnologist and psychoanalyst Derek Freeman have shown that hunting is so intricately interwoven with the whole social system of some Bornean tribes that its abolition tends to disintegrate their whole culture, even seriously jeopardizing the survival of the people. (p. 261)

In actual fact the abolition of the traditional culture of Bornean head-hunters has been accompanied by an upsurge of population of embarrassing dimensions.

Nevertheless, careful reflection upon just what *is* the distinction between species difference in animals and cultural difference in man is badly needed, and the ethologists' brash comments on the matter should help to clarify the anthropologists' discussions. Even Ardrey's profound confusions, by which he claims to explain the passing fashions of international politics as a simple response to genetic drives, could serve some useful purpose if it leads a more serious author to tackle what is certainly a very serious subject.

Ardrey's argument runs something like this. The ethologists have shown that the phenomenon of territoriality recurs throughout the animal kingdom. Individual members of a particular species identify with a particular territory. All other members of the same species are dichotomized as friends and strangers. Strangers are attacked if they intrude on *our* territory; the deeper the intrusion the more violent the counter aggression. "This vital mode of behavior is not learned by the individual but is innate in the species." Ardrey then makes two kinds of mistake. In the first place he usually writes as if this kind of behavior were found in *all* animals and that, therefore, it *must* be characteristic of man also. This is an error of fact. Secondly he confuses the behavior as such with the circumstances that produce it. He thinks that the statement "aggressive behavior is innate" conflicts with J. P. Scott's proposition that "all stimulation of aggression eventually comes from forces present in the external environment." This is not the case. If we define the word "aggression" in a behavioristic way, as an ethologist should, then man, like any other animal, has built-in "innate" ways of exhibiting aggression. What is in dispute is whether man likewise has a built-in tendency to defend his home territory so that the precise circumstances in which he will exhibit this "aggressive behavior" are predictable. Ardrey is well aware of the weakness of his case. He knows (pp. 220-224) that man's nearest living cousins, the anthropoid apes, show no such tendency, but he blandly assures us that these pacifist animals are "evolutionary failures"! He writes luridly of our "human" ancestors of two million years ago: "Far from being a beginner at the killing game . . . this pygmy sized predator of the high savannah was a skilled and successful hunter of what men today would still call big game . . . we killed animals ten or twenty times our size, did we kill each other?" And, of course, Ardrey's answer is "yes," the whole fantasy resting on a quite uncritical interpretation of a single fossil ape-like skull of a creature whose relationship to modern man is obscure but certainly not close.

Lorenz's comment is much to the point. If proto-man had been at all like the figment of Ardrey's imagination he would have wiped himself out of existence. The survivors in the evolutionary rat-race are of two kinds—those which are disinclined to kill at all and those which are inclined to kill but are inhibited against killing members of their own kind. The uninhibited killer is a non-starter. Natural man, in Lorenz's view, is a pacific creature; pit two unarmed individual men against each other in an unconfined space and the odds are heavy that both will survive. Man only becomes dangerous when he is equipped with weapons, and weapons are a product of culture, not of nature. But this is where the application of ethological arguments to the human situation becomes really interesting. And it is just here that Ardrey misses the point.

Evolutionary theory does not at all suggest that the "successful" species are those gifted with "killing propensity." Very much the reverse. Species become differentiated by specialized adaptation to territorially isolated ecological conditions. The attachment of an individual to its home territory is directly linked up with this process of adaptive specialization. In such cases Ardrey's "territorial imperative" does have important evolutionary consequences. But one of the special peculiarities of the species *Homo sapiens* is its lack of ecological specialization. No other species can adjust so readily to drastic variations of temperature, humidity, and diet. And this highly advantageous plasticity is tied in with the fact that man, as a species, is almost entirely free from territorial limitations and attachments. It is true that living human beings, both as individuals and as groups, do on occasion exhibit symptoms resembling the "territoriality" displayed by various species of birds and fish, but this human behavior is a cultural not a species characteristic, and this makes all the difference. It is optional not "instinctive" behavior. Sovereignty is not a new idea, but it is not a human universal.

But let us go back to man and his weapons. It begins to look as if man and his proto-human ancestors have been using tools and weapons for several million years. Several crucial peculiarities of man—capacity for speech, upright gait, marked sexual dimorphism, absence of seasonal sexuality, lack of fur, peculiar placement of the sexual organs, etc.—are adaptive peculiarities which have evolved in the context of a natural environment modified by the existence of weapons and tools. Man did not evolve as a complete human being and *then* acquire speech and culture. He developed speech and culture while still evolving as an animal species. And our human predicament is that this process still goes on. Other animals adapt to a specialized environment which is relatively stable. If the environment changes drastically the species usually becomes extinct. In contrast, man's adaptive apparatus includes a technology which changes the environment as it goes along. Man and his environment are thus *always* out of step. As Lorenz puts it, "the extreme speed of ecological and sociological change wrought by the developments of technology causes many customs to become maladaptive within one generation." He finds the pace too hot, and it fills him with anxiety. I find this odd, but it shows up a glaring weakness in current ethological fashion. Students of animal behavior are so accustomed to finding a perfect fit between the innate capacities of a species and its total environment that they are inclined to view as pathological any palpable lack of fit between the state of human society and the state of the geographical space within which it exists. This is the classic fallacy of functionalist sociology all over again. Lorenz's word "maladaptive" turns up in contexts where Durkheim would have written "anomie"; Georg Simmel was making Lorenz's point about the positive function of conflict nearly sixty years ago; for sociologists, Malinowski's notion that, in a healthy society, social norms must always fit with the requirements of ecology and of human biological needs has been a dead duck for nearly a generation.

Certainly the observation of animals may have moral lessons for human beings—"Go to the ant, thou sluggard, consider her ways and be wise"—but we shall only deceive ourselves if we attempt to minimize the differences between human and non-human animal behavior. The development of speech in *Homo sapiens* has completely altered our nature. A goose can communicate with another goose by means of "ritualized" gestures, but the kinds of message it can transmit are very narrowly delimited: "Hostility" and "friendship" are only the observer's labels for simple triggered responses. In contrast, human beings can say an infinite number of things in an infinite number of different ways; responses are intrinsically unpredictable; politicians and historians are what they are precisely because no man can ever know what his "opponent" is going to do next.

Relations of solidarity and opposition, amity and hostility, gift exchange and war, constitute the basic subject matter of sociological enquiry, and only a very simple-minded man could suppose that such complex matters might be readily understood by simple analogy with the habits of the prairie-dog. But this is what Ardrey implies. It is perfectly true that, as members of a common species *Homo sapiens,* we are all predisposed to behave in certain fixed ways which reflect our biochemical constitutions. But this in itself does not tell us very much. We are all naturally endowed with a capacity for speech and all spoken languages have certain features in common—e.g., they convey meaning by means of an alternation of vowels and consonants—but these constraints set no limit on what we say. Likewise the physical gestures of *Homo* are limited in kind by the fact that the actor is a man and not a goose. But what we express by these gestures is not limited at all. Thus any belief that our customs are somehow predetermined in the same sense as are the mating rituals of birds is an illusion.

The argument is in some respects circular. The ethologists interpret particular animal behaviors as *aggressive, amicable, dominant, submissive,* etc., and they use such terms because of what they know intuitively about themselves. That being so, it is quite illogical to reverse the process and pretend that we might understand human aggression better because of its analogic similarity to "animal aggression." Until he reaches Chapter 13 Lorenz only occasionally falls into this fallacy. Most of his book is an entrancing record of how human observers can make objective studies of relationships between animals. But Ardrey's anthropomorphism is of the clumsiest kind. He has a nursery-floor view of human affairs: "The principal cause of modern warfare arises from the failure of an intruding power correctly to estimate the defensive resources of a territorial defender." Ethology apart, this is the Hobbesian notion that if there were no policemen, each of us would immediately set about murdering everyone else in sight, and it is total rubbish.

To sum up, the Lorenz book is delightful and fascinating, as long as the author sticks to his own field; away off when he starts mixing in anthropology or politics or philosophy. In the Ardrey version the mixture of extraneous matter is so great that it is best left alone altogether.

Ardrey on Human Nature:
Animals, Nations, Imperatives

Almost without question, Robert Ardrey is today the most influential writer in English dealing with the innate or instinctive attributes of human nature, and the most skilled populariser of the findings of paleo-anthropologists, ethologists, and biological experimenters. As a populariser, he covers some of the same material as, for example, Arthur Koestler. He is a skilled writer, with a lively command of English prose, a pretty turn of wit, and a dramatist's skill in exposition; he is also a good reporter, with the reporter's eye for the significant detail, the striking visual impression. He has taken a look at nearly all the current work in Africa of paleo-anthropologists and ethologists; time and again, a couple of his paragraphs can make vivid a site, such as the Olduvai Gorge, which has been merely a name in a hundred articles. His wide readership has been earned, at least in part, by his mastery of the writer's crafts.

His first, almost accidental, encounter with Africa was, he tells us, as a journalist. His two books on scientific themes are largely autobiographical, a fact which is emphasised in the sub-title of each: *African Genesis* (1961) is subtitled "A Personal Investigation into the Animal Origins and Nature of Man"; and *The Terri-*

From *Encounter*, June 1967. Copyright © 1967 by Geoffrey Gorer. Reprinted by permission of Harold Ober Associates Inc.

torial Imperative (1967) "A Personal Inquiry into the Animal Origins of Property and Nations." It would not be unfair to say that he is conducting his adult education in public. In the course of the two books he tells us a good deal about himself.

He was born in Chicago's South Side in 1908, his family being of Scottish origin. He was educated in Chicago, apparently taking some course in social science under Professor Ogburn; he graduated during the depression, and for a short time earned his living as a lecturer in anthropology at the Chicago World's Fair and as a self-described statistician; these were his only contacts with the social sciences for twenty years. He became a playwright who was esteemed, if not markedly successful, was awarded a Guggenheim fellowship, and then moved to Hollywood as a professional scriptwriter. Apart from World War II, when he was in an overseas branch of the Office of War Information, this work continued until 1954. He then became unemployed, his new Broadway play was a flop, and he was engaged by the editor of *The Reporter* to do a series of articles on Africa, particularly the Mau Mau rising. Almost by accident, he was asked to interview the Australian-born South African paleo-anthropologist, Raymond Dart.

In February 1955, Dart gave him a fossilised jawbone of *australopithecus* to hold; this experience became Ardrey's Road to Damascus. In a flash, it would seem, the orientation of his life was changed: his aim in life was no longer to entertain but to educate (in the first place, himself). He had felt immediate conviction of the correctness of Dart's interpretation of his australopithecine and associated fossils; and it became his mission to rescue Dart from the neglect and contumely which his unorthodox interpretations had gained from the academic world of paleo-anthropology. In this he has been markedly successful.

It is a typical sequel to conversion that the convert feels compelled to share his illumination with the benighted; and Ardrey writes with much the same conviction of having achieved access to deeper truths as do converts to the older established religions or to Marxism or psycho-analysis or "psychodelic" drugs; it is this feeling of urgency which helps give Ardrey's books their compulsive readability. But, although the convert feels that he is completely changed, he brings to his new life his old habits and skills. Ardrey was a dramatist; and one of the characteristics of dramatists is to put a very great load of significance on to a few symbols or metaphors, a far greater load than they would bear outside the condensation of a play. Nearly all my criticism of Ardrey's ideas derives from his tendency to overload symbols and metaphors, to use the same phrases in a very wide variety of contexts and with very different significants.

As far as I can check, Ardrey is a first-class conscientious reporter. He looks and listens and notes with care and precision; he is extremely diligent in his reading and research; and he does not distort his authorities beyond what is inevitable in any selection and condensation. One can question his selection of topics to emphasise or to ignore; but, to the best of my knowledge, he never ascribes to a scientist an observation or conclusion he has not made. He has read extremely widely in his selected topics of paleoanthroplogy and ethology; even those familiar with most of the literature are likely to find descriptions of research they had hitherto ignored, particularly in *The Territorial Imperative,* with its bibliography of 245 items.

Unfortunately, Ardrey's diligence and research has so far stopped short at *Homo sapiens.* His views on human behaviour are almost entirely impressionistic, embued with the sophistication of a cosmopolitan writer who reads news magazines. Like most dramatists he writes as though he had an intuitive insight into human motivation; and like most autobiographers he believes that he is a typical example of human nature, but more honest than most. He is reliable when he discusses *proconsul* or *australopithecus,* the birds and the bees, mice and monkeys, for he relies on expert authorities; when he discusses man he relies on himself.

The argument of both books is that we will arrive at a more rational understanding of contemporary man if we study man's instinctual endowment; and that this instinctual endowment can be learned from the study of the remains of pre-hominids and early hominids and the behaviour of other vertebrates. Our knowledge of human evolution and of animal behaviour has increased so enormously in the last thirty years that Ardrey is justified in writing of a "scientific revolution" and he has brought this knowledge to the attention of the literate English-speaking public as no other populariser has done. Konrad Lorenz has a large audience; but, like many another genius, he has paid relatively little attention to independent work done in his field.

Ardrey's moment of illumination came when Raymond Dart demonstrated to him that *Australopithecus africanus*—one of the very early primates—had been a carnivorous predator who was bipedal and selected and used the humerus of one antelope and the mandible of another as weapons. In his 1953 paper, *The Predatory Transition from Ape to Man,* Dart had argued that the hominisation of the pre-hominids had been facilitated by the change, in one line of australopithecines, from a vegetarian to a flesh diet; the use of weapons had led to a bipedal stance, the development of the thumb, eventually the enlargement of the brain. In Ardrey's words:

> Far from the truth lay the antique assumption that man had fathered the weapon. The weapon, instead, had fathered man. The mightiest of predators had come about as the logical conclusion to an evolutionary transition. With his big brain and his stone handaxes, man annihilated a predecessor who fought only with bones. And if all human history from that date has turned on the development of superior weapons, then it is for very sound reason. It is for genetic necessity. We design and compete with our weapons as birds build distinctive nests.

This short quotation shows both the strength and weaknesses of Ardrey's methods. In the study of human evolution Dart's work was both novel and disturbing; it was almost completely neglected when Ardrey first wrote, and is still not universally accepted. It was valuable to bring this material to wider notice.

None of the later sentences is justified by the evidence. There is nothing to suggest that *Australopithecus africanus* and *Homo sapiens* were contemporaries, and that therefore the latter "annihilated" the former. The bones which *Australopithecus* selected were implements for killing other species, not for killing co-specifics. Weapons, in human history, are entirely designed for killing co-specifics; in all societies of any technological complexity there is a distinction between implements for hunting and implements for war; rarely do the two overlap. Birds which build distinctive nests are of different species (or sub-species) and are not competing against one another; man is a single species.

Although Dart's material demands a most drastic revision of previously held views of human evolution and hominisation, it does not demand a revision of our views of human instinctual endowment even if, which is still unproven, *Australopithecus africanus* were some day to be established as directly ancestral to *Homo sapiens*. It has long been generally accepted that early man was a carnivorous predator who used hunting implements to kill other species for food; if pre-hominids did do the same, it does not make man any more, or any less, "a killer." This phrase, loaded with ambiguity, is a favourite of Ardrey's. All meat-eaters (scavengers appear to be only a partial exception) are "killers" of other species for their food; among the mammals there is no clear evidence for any species being "killers" of their co-specifics intentionally, other than rats and men.

Ardrey thinks that this new material demands a complete revision of human instinctual endowment, that it shows that man is instinctually a killer with an innate propensity for using weapons against his fellow-man; and, more reasonably, that the notions of Special Creation, or of Original Goodness, are now untenable. The final chapter of *African Genesis* is entitled "Children of Cain" * and argues that man has "an aggressive imperative" and cannot survive without war and the weapons of war. Organised warfare between states is, of course, a very modern human invention, subsequent to the neolithic revolution of about 10,000 years ago when the first nation-states were established; it is a source of considerable ambiguity to use the same term for the short skirmishes between a few people which typify primitive "war" and the wars between nation-states as we have known them in recent millennia.

Besides the information on paleo-anthropology and his deductions therefrom, Ardrey deals with many themes in *African Genesis* which he takes up again in greater detail in *The Territorial Imperative;* he also has one chapter, very richly illustrated, on status, dominance, and deference within animal societies. His de-

---

* This phrase is a typically misapplied cliché. If Ardrey had gone back to his sources (*Genesis:* 4) he would have found that Cain was a vegetarian, not a carnivore, and so, if you will, the descendant of *paranthropus;* Abel was the carnivorous descendant of *Australopithecus africanus;* and Cain killed him because Jehovah preferred meat to vegetables. The mark of Cain was to prevent anyone else killing him; and there is nothing in the Bible to suggest that Cain ever killed a second time.

duction from this material is "that among all animal sources of human behaviour, the instinct for status may in the end prove the most important." To date, this assertion is not backed by any study of human behavior; but it is interesting to note how Ardrey finds ethological justification for all the values of "rugged individualism."

The Territorial Imperative is a much more important and thorough book; Ardrey is justified in his claim that this is the first book since 1920 to deal comprehensively with the concept of territory. He has drawn very widely on the scattered and copious literature. He defines his topic as follows:

> A territory is an area of space, whether of water or earth or air, which an animal or group of animals defends as an exclusive preserve. The word is also used to describe the inward compulsion in animate beings to possess and defend such a space. A territorial species of animals, therefore, is one in which all the males, and sometimes females too, bear an inherent drive to gain and defend an exclusive property.

Under this definition, a majority of the vertebrate species so far studied and some invertebrate species are territorial animals; it is highly likely that some analogue to this instinct is also part of man's instinctual endowment. But territory is used by Ardrey, and by many of the ethologists he quotes, in a highly ambiguous fashion; it is a word of multiple meanings, which are seldom explicitly distinguished.

The word was first introduced into modern studies of animals by H. E. Howard, whose observations were based on British birds. Birds may have four types of territory: (1) the nest or breeding area, which is nearly universal; Ardrey quotes Howard as stating that a male with a mate and no territory is a natural impossibility. Territory (2) is an area surrounding the nest which will be defended against intrusion from male co-specifics. The song and bright plumage of the male are, quite probably, a warning to other males not to trespass; if trespass does occur, it is always successfully repulsed. Territory (2) varies in its extent from species to species. Predators often have territory (3), an exclusive hunting area. Finally a few species, such as blackcock, ruffs, sage grouse, and bower birds have territory (4), a copulating area (the lek of the black-cock) where only those dominant males who have acquired a stamping ground are selected by the females for mates. This rare type of territory is also found among the Uganda Kob, a species of antelope; this was first observed and reported by Helmut K. Buechner; Ardrey visited the rutting areas (which he calls "are-nas") and gives a vivid and fascinating account of them. Social mammals, including most of the anthropoids, have a variation of territory (3) in which the hunting or food-gathering area is shared and defended by more than one adult male and their mates and young.

While territories (1) and (2) are occupied and defended, the occupier can be considered the proprietor, and the territory its property. But this proprietorship differs in many ways from "pri-vate property" as understood in the modern world. It is not alien-able or heritable and must be continuously defended or "earned." The data do not suggest that the territorial instinct is a natural validation of the ownership of transferable property by human beings. The demand for territory (1), a private breeding ground, does seem to be nearly a human universal; even those societies which have "long houses," or other types of extended-family dwell-ings, provide a private breeding area by means of walls or parti-tions. A society which fails to provide adequate breeding areas for the newly mated may well evoke deep feelings.

As far as social mammals are concerned, territory (3), the hunt-ing and food-gathering territory, is almost always shared; rather than an analogue to private property, territory (3) is an analogue to common land, to socialised ownership.

Ardrey introduces two terms of his own to describe the spacing of territories (1) and (2) and the defence of territory (3) re-spectively. When breeding territories are close together, as in the breeding colonies of many seabirds, and the occupants of these ter-ritories spend more energy in mutual disputes, in inward-directed antagonism, rather than in defence of the colony's territories against other co-specifics, he uses the term *noyau*. He has taken this term from J. J. Petter, who used it to describe the behaviour of one of the nocturnal species of lemur in Madagascar. It is quite a useful term for describing a fairly uncommon type of mammalian, and a fairly common type of avian, behaviour; but it is a metaphor of very doubtful validity when transferred to human beings. Some types of clique could perhaps be so described without stretching the analogy too far. But to write "Italy is a *noyau*. It is not a nation" tells us nothing about Italy, though something about Ardrey's preferences and prejudices.

"Nation" or "biological nation" is the other term which Ardrey has introduced to describe mammalian defence of territory (3).

> The biological nation, as I define it in this work, is a social group containing at least two mature males which holds as an exclusive possession a continuous area of space, which isolates itself from others of its kind through outward antagonism, and which through joint defence of its social territory achieves leadership, cooperation, and a capacity for concerted action. It does not matter too much whether such a nation be composed of twenty-five individuals or two hundred and fifty million.

There is no justification in any ethological writing, as far as I am aware (and Ardrey quotes none) for applying the term "nation" to any animal grouping; and since this is a word in common use with an accepted meaning,* to give it a private significance is treating words as Humpty Dumpty did ("When *I* use a word it means just what I choose it to mean—neither more nor less") and far from the responsible behaviour of a scientist or of a writer dealing with scientific subjects.† The confusion is compounded because on occasion (*e.g.*, p. 214) Ardrey uses "nation" and "society" as synonyms when discussing animals. He also transfers what he has learnt from ethologists about the defence of territory (3) by social animals to some contemporary nation-states without modification. This renders the three final chapters of *The Territorial Imperative* seriously misleading.

When he discusses the contemporary scene, Ardrey reserves the term "biological nation" for those states whose military conduct he

---

* The Shorter Oxford English Dictionary gives the definition: "A distinct race of people, characterised by common descent, language or history usually organised as a separate political state and occupying a definite territory." It quotes as an obsolete meaning "A particular class, kind or race of persons or of animals."

† An analogy could perhaps be drawn between introducing a concept into a context where it does not belong and introducing a skull into a stratum where it does not belong, as happened at Piltdown.

approves of. The United States of America is of course the "biological nation" *par excellence* (he does not explain the appropriateness of the adjective to a nation of immigrants and immigrants' children); but Britain, Finland, Greece, and some other societies of Northern Europe also qualify. Italy, as we have seen, is a *"noyau . . . not a nation."* "France, in the years between the wars had slipped, like Italy, to the status of a *noyau,* the society of inward antagonism which it yet, in all probability, remains." Black Africa has no nations: "none of the new states remotely resembled biological nations"; but white South Africa (pp. 315–17) is most emphatically a "biological nation." The one exception to the apparent generalisation that only white-skinned Protestant Nordics are capable of composing "biological nations" is that the same distinction is accorded to Israel; but the re-territorialisation of the Jews has made the "Jewish personality" disappear (pp. 307–12).

These three final chapters are so full of oversimplifications, questionable statements, omissions and plain inaccuracies that it would take a second comment as long as this to list and analyse them. Ardrey shows only the most superficial knowledge of contemporary events, practically no knowledge of the history of the old world or of contemporary sociology and social anthropology. His categories and preferences are bound to give comfort and provide ammunition for the radical Right, for the Birchites and Empire Loyalists and their analogues elsewhere; there is, however, no evidence to show that Ardrey himself holds or advocates any such political views. His dramatist's employment of ambiguous metaphors and symbols has brought him to these ambiguous conclusions.

Ardrey has done a service to the literate English-reading public by making the novel findings of ethologists and biologists so vividly available. This service would have been far greater if he had confined himself to the animals, and omitted his views on *Homo sapiens.* As it is, *The Territorial Imperative* demands a wrapper: "Handle carefully. Read with critical scepticism."

KENNETH E. BOULDING

Am I a Man or a Mouse—or Both?

Two recent books by Konrad Lorenz and Robert Ardrey have
aroused a great deal of discussion and have raised at least by implication some important questions. Lorenz is a very distinguished
Austrian ethologist who has made a life-long work out of studying
animal behavior. His earlier book, *King Solomon's Ring,* is a classic in the field. I am not professionally equipped to assess his scientific contributions, but to judge from some of the scientific reviews,
Lorenz is a pioneer in the field of the study of animal behavior,
that is, ethology, but like many pioneers he is now regarded as
somewhat old-fashioned by the rising generation striding forward
into the field. But whatever may be the scientific merits of Lorenz,
the literary merits are unquestionable. He writes with great vigor
and charm and opens up new and exciting worlds to the reader.
The animal world is never the same again after one has read Lorenz; he opens one's eyes to its richness and complexity.

Ardrey is not a scientist but a playwright and a moralist, though
it would be legitimate to describe him as a popularizer of science.
He has both read and listened widely. Nevertheless, he almost literally has an axe to grind and enters the courtroom of the mind, as it
were, with a brief. His style, while it is readable and has a superficial charm, often seems to me to weaken itself by straining for
effect, and does not have the effortless grace of Lorenz. His works,

From *War/Peace Report,* March 1967, pp. 14–17. Reprinted by permission.

furthermore, betray a life-long love affair with himself which gets rather tiresome, and he can be irritating enough to make one want to throw the book across the room. However, he has something to say, and his brief at least deserves to be examined carefully and judged in the light of further evidence.

There are many things common to these two books, which is not surprising, as they both deal with essentially the same subject of animal behavior. Both deal with aggression in animals, although neither of them defines it. Both are concerned with territoriality, that is, the tendency that many animals have either as individuals, as pairs or as groups, to stake out a territory in the environment, mark it with some distinguishing odor or disfigurement, and defend it against intruders of the same species. Where the theme of territoriality is central to Ardrey, to Lorenz it is merely part of a much larger problem of conflict management within a species, having many other aspects. Both the authors are naturally concerned with the processes of evolution, especially of genetic or biologic evolution, and neither of the authors hesitates to make a great leap from animals to man or from genetic evolution into cultural evolution, and to draw conclusions about man from the behavior of animals. It is this last aspect of the work which has aroused most of the controversy and to which I propose to devote most attention, though it should be noted that the strictly ethological material of these works is by no means immune from criticism, for ethology is a young and rapidly advancing science and has still explored only a very imperfect and probably biased sample of its field.

What Can We Learn?

Let me begin then by raising the central question of what we can learn about man and the social system by the study of animals and animal society, before we examine in detail the conclusions which these authors have drawn. There is no doubt, of course, that a man is a physiological organization produced by a growth process which is largely organized by characteristics coded into the total genetic structure of the fertilized egg. The characteristics contained in man's genetic code are accumulated over billions of years and are the end result of a very complex process of mutation and selection. We could in theory postulate an unbroken genetic chain from the primordial amoeba or whatever it was that started life to any individual person existing today. The further back we go in this sequence of genetic structures, presumably the simpler they get in terms of the characteristics they code. Presumably the genetic structure of an amoeba is much simpler than that of a fish, a fish simpler than that of a monkey, a monkey simpler than that of a man.

There are probably no representatives around today of organizations of the identical genetic composition of man's ancestors. Even the amoeba today is probably a little different from the one-celled organism of two billion or more years ago from which we sprang, but nevertheless there are parallels. Some branches of the great tree of evolution have changed less than others. The amoeba today, therefore, is probably a good deal like man's one-celled ancestors, the fish of today may resemble man's fishy ancestors and the monkeys of today have some similarities with man's simian ancestors. This is one conceivable justification for the belief that the study of animal behavior will throw light on human behavior. By studying the behavior of simpler living organisms, we may be able to perceive patterns which may have been present in our ancestors and which may therefore also be present in the complex system of man himself.

We can see immediately, however, how dangerous the method of analogy may be. None of man's direct genetic ancestors are any longer around. Their behavior cannot be studied, though their bones may be. The monkeys of today may have diverged almost as much from their ancestors of two million years ago as man has diverged from his. In jumping from monkeys to man, therefore, we are really making two leaps in the dark, one from the monkey back to man's common ancestor, and again from this ancestor to man. A leap in the dark, of course, may land us on the right side of the pit, but it has to be scrutinized with unusual care to be sure that we have not fallen into serious error. The greatest danger here is from leaping from the simple to the complex, for it is precisely what is not in the simple system that may constitute the essential character of the complex. Hence, even if the simple system is itself embodied in the complex one, this fact only carries us a very little way toward understanding the nature and behavior of the complex.

We could perhaps draw a parallel here from the evolution of

man's artifacts, which follow a course of mutation and selection not unlike that of biological evolution. There is a kind of genetic chain in man's imagination and skill leading from the flint knife to the metal axe to the pneumatic drill to the modern coal-mining machine. Also, shall we say, from the wheelbarrow to the cart to the automobile to the jet plane. The problem with deducing the nature of the artifacts of primitive times from those which are around today is not so difficult, especially as primitive artifacts have left a good many traces. The critical question is how much we could learn about the jet plane from studying the wheelbarrow or even from studying the automobile; if the jet plane is man, the automobile perhaps is the mammal, the wheelbarrow the fish, in terms of relative complexity of system.

Nobody would deny that we could find out something about the jet plane by studying the wheelbarrow. We could find out perhaps about metals and about wheels, but we certainly would not find out about flight. An even better comparison would be between a one-task machine like a loom and the modern computer that is capable of learning and can be programmed to innumerable tasks. Because a loom has a shuttle are we to say a computer must also have a shuttle, or some analog of it? Similarly, if displaced aggression in the goose leads to love, as Lorenz says it does, or if territoriality is a characteristic of the Uganda kob, as Ardrey describes, does this mean either that man's ancestors possessed these qualities and attributes or that man today does? It is clear that a great leap has been made in the dark but it is by no means clear that our feet have landed on firm ground.

The crux of the matter, of course, is the old argument about nature and nurture, heredity and environment, instinct and learning. There is little doubt that the oriole's genes build into the bird itself both the knowledge and the desire to build an oriole nest and that this knowledge comes from the information in the gene rather than information coming into the bird through its senses. It is the great peculiarity of man, however, differentiating him from all the other animals, that what his genes endow him with is an enormous nervous system of some 10 billion components, the informational content of which is derived almost wholly from the environment, that is, from inputs into the organism from outside. The genetic contribution to man's nervous system is virtually complete at birth. Almost everything that happens thereafter is learned. It is this consideration which inspires the modern anthropologist to declare that man has virtually no instincts and that virtually everything he knows has to be learned from his environment, which consists both of the physical world in which he lives and moves and the social world into which he is born. It is this characteristic that differentiates cultural evolution from biological evolution. The time seems to be approaching, indeed, when cultural evolution will dominate biological evolution because man will acquire power to manipulate the gene pool directly. Up to now he has not been able to do this, but even so, in at least the last ten thousand years the cultural evolution has dominated the scene, transmitting information through the learning process and not through the information coded in the genes.

The critical question here is the extent to which the genetic composition of the human body limits and determines what it can learn from its environment. That such limits exist there can be no doubt, for no man has an indefinite capacity for learning. Furthermore, it is clear that genetic defects which, for instance, produce the mongoloid or the idiot, result in a very serious limitation of the potential field of learning, even though there is a good deal of evidence accumulating that this limitation itself is a function of the culture into which the child grows and may be less confining than we now think. We are pretty sure that it is genetic constitution which prevents a dog or a chimpanzee from learning to talk; we are not quite so sure about the dolphin. What does seem to be clear, however, is that for the normal human being the limits on learning imposed by the physiological constitution of the human nervous system are very far out, and that most of the limits come from a dynamic failure of the learning process in experience rather than from any limitations imposed by the physiological nature of the human nervous system, the capacity of which seems very far from having been exhausted. It is, indeed, the existence of large excess capacity in the human nervous system which it seems to me vitiates the arguments of those who seek to find in "instinct" any explanation whatever of human behavior beyond the most elementary and primitive acts of the newly born.

The argument is complicated, however, by the fact that environments themselves can breed. Culture is a body of coded information which is passed on from generation to generation, suffering mutation and selection, just as the coded information in the gene is passed on, except that cultural evolution is much more subject to mutation and proceeds at a much more rapid rate than the evolution of the genetic structure. Consequently, the concept of a cultural instinct is by no means absurd, even though the genes of culture are much less stable and much more subject to mutation than the biological genes. We have not learned aggression, however, from our remote biological ancestors, nor have we learned territoriality from them. Insofar as aggression or territoriality play a part in human culture—and they do—each generation learns them from the previous generation and perhaps in a lesser degree from its own physical environment and random events.

A change in human affairs comes hardly at all from changes in the gene pool and its distribution in mankind, though this cannot be wholly excluded. Genetic changes do take place slowly as previously isolated gene pools intermingle through the breakdown of concepts of caste and race, as aristocracies fail to reproduce themselves, and as peasants multiply, but it would be surprising if these factors accounted for more than a fraction of one per cent of social change and social evolution. It is new inputs of information into a culture that constitute mutation in social evolution and these inputs can affect either the image of the world or the value systems, according to which decisions are made. Human aggression and human territoriality are products of social systems, not of biological systems, and they must be treated as such, even though concepts and analogies which are derived from biological systems may occasionally be helpful. The naive analogizing, therefore, even of Lorenz and especially of Ardrey will not stand up to a moment's serious criticism.

An Ideological Need

In light of the fact that these works have been rejected by the scientific community almost without exception as serious scientific documents, at least in regard to the conclusions which they draw about society, it is important to ask why they have received so much attention and why they seem to meet an ideological need, especially in the United States. This is a question, unfortunately, to which a fairly clear answer can be given out of the analysis of social systems. I say unfortunately, because the answer is a disagreeable one, but I see no way of escaping it. By a very complex series of events the "establishment" of American society, that is, those people who are either important decision-makers or close to them or identified with them have "learned" that the international system is primarily a "threat system" and that threats must be made credible by occasionally carrying them out, even though this involves inflicting appalling suffering upon innocent people.

The war in Vietnam can only be interpreted as an attempt to make the American threat system credible by demonstrating our willingness to be cruel and merciless so that people will believe the threat implicit in our enormous military establishment. To be effective, however, it is not enough that threats should be credible; they also should have to be legitimate, especially in the minds of the threatener himself, for unless he feels that his cruelty is justified he will find it hard to continue in it. The rise of Hitler and of Pearl Harbor in the 1930s and early '40s taught this country that naive idealism did not pay so we decided to throw away the idealism.

On the other hand, idealism of some sort is necessary for justification and legitimation, for no line of policy can be pursued for very long without self-justification. A line of argument like that of Ardrey's, therefore, seems to legitimate our present morality, in regarding the threat system as dominant at all costs, by reference to our biological ancestors. If the names of both antiquity and of science can be drawn upon to legitimate our behavior, the moral uneasiness about napalm and the massacre of the innocent in Vietnam may be assuaged. Dr. Lorenz, I am sure, who is a gentle, humane soul, still, one would judge, living in the afterglow of Franz Josef, would be horrified by this suggestion. Nevertheless, one cannot altogether absolve even Dr. Lorenz (to whom I owe some of the most delightful hours of my reading life), from the sin of using the prestige of one science to jump to unwarranted conclusions in another, and hence to bring the weight of scientific authority behind essentially unproven propositions. In Ardrey's case the need for legitimation is more obvious, and there are real dangers of a pseudo-science used to bolster and legitimate an otherwise untenable moral position. Even Ardrey, however, I am sure, is a decent fellow at heart, and is on the side of man. Nevertheless, the pit that he is leaping over in the dark is very wide and destruction lurks at the bottom, and those who have the interests both of science and mankind at heart at least need to turn on their flashlights.

We have seen in the Nazi movement how appallingly dangerous a pseudo-science can be in the legitimation of an absurd and evil system. I am not suggesting that either Lorenz or Ardrey is a racist theorist like Gobineau or Houston Chamberlain. However, one could imagine their superficially attractive neo-social-Darwinism applied to very ill uses indeed, and the fact that it is scientific humbug does not unfortunately detract from its attractiveness.

SIR SOLLY ZUCKERMAN

The Human Beast

Konrad Lorenz is a name to conjure with in the world of animal psychology, where he is celebrated as the originator of "ethology." It is under this description that he has helped to make the study of the social relationships of animals so popular in recent years.

In a foreword to *On Aggression* Julian Huxley writes that Lorenz's basic contribution to science is his interpretation of vertebrate behaviour in terms of the interaction of behaviour-units which, like the structural "units" of the body, are subject to evolutionary modification through genetic change and natural selection. He is equally famed because of his formulation of the concept of "unit releasers" of behaviour patterns, and through his studies of the process of "imprinting" or "object fixation"—a process which was, of course, known long before his time, and whereby, to give a famous Lorenzian illustration, a newly hatched gosling attaches itself, as though to its mother, to the person or creature by whom it is first cared for and fed—no doubt in the same way as Mary's little lamb attached itself to Mary. Above all, Lorenz is known and revered because every page of his widely read popular writings reveals a rich personality and a sensitive love of animals.

In its original German, and in an American edition, *On Aggression* has already attracted wide attention. The basic theme is that the forms of behaviour which the author calls aggression need to

From *Nature*, November 5, 1966, pp. 563–64. Reprinted by permission.

be differentiated from those which characterize predation. To Lorenz there has been no aggression when a lion fells a buffalo, although aggression characterizes the behaviour of the buffalo, either alone or in groups, when it tries to fight off the lion. By definition it is only the members of the same species who are aggressive to each other, and in some species aggression does not occur at all. Too much intraspecific aggression could lead to the extermination of the species, and the units of behaviour which constitute aggression become modified and ritualized by natural selection. In their transformed state they serve a useful but now harmless purpose in a different behavioural context. By analysing the phylogeny of ritual and harmless animal behaviour one can often trace its origin to the components of aggression.

Within the "biotope" in which a species lives, individuals settle in territories of their own which they defend against intruders with an intensity which Lorenz states increases geometrically from the periphery to the centre of the home ground. (How this has been measured is not stated.) This kind of intraspecific aggression leads to the even distribution of individuals over the whole area in which the species is found, and also to the "selection" of males as the begetters of the next generation which are better in a variety of ways than those which fail to stand up to the pressures of intraspecific aggression. The latter thus results in one form of sexual selection. Another operates in some species through the female, who responds to the secondary sexual characters of the male even when the latter have evolved, as a consequence of exaggerated patterns of sexual display, to the point when they are an actual physical handicap—as in the case of the magnificent secondary wing feathers of the Argus cock pheasant. Correspondingly, through phylogenetic "ritualization," the units of aggressive behaviour can be so transformed that the male which would otherwise set on, and try to rout, any intruder into his territory, learns to accept the female.

In the interests of survival, natural selection thus brings about remarkable transformations in, and restraints to, the exercise of the component units of compulsive pugnacious behaviour, and these transformations endlessly enrich the manifestations of nature's wildlife. They include even such phenomena as individual love and friendship—emotions which develop only in the most aggressive species.

This, broadly, is the picture of animal social life which Lorenz sets as a screen against which to consider man's social and political problems. He sees the fighting of cocks in a barnyard as one end of a spectrum of aggressive behaviour, the other reaching "to barroom brawls about politics, and finally to wars and atom bombs." Unhappily, according to Lorenz, man suffers the immense disadvantage that he is ill equipped to ritualize his aggressive instinct. It is our misfortune to be "a basically harmless, omnivorous creature, lacking in natural weapons with which to kill big prey, and, therefore, also devoid of the built-in safety devices which prevent 'professional' carnivores from abusing their killing power to destroy fellow-members of their own species." Therefore, to avoid the ultimate extermination of our species in a nuclear holocaust, it is urgent that we make a determined effort to sublimate our aggressive instincts in cultural pursuits and in activities such as international sporting contests. Widespread participation in biological research would also help—this would lead to better understanding of the causes of the aggressive attitudes of nations. And with this prescription for our ills, Lorenz leaves us.

Judged as a piece of writing, as a work of rich and compelling description, the book deserves all praise. But it is hardly a serious work of science, which one assumes is what Lorenz intended. For all the wealth of observation it retails, its choice of material is highly selective, and its generalizations so sweeping that it becomes difficult to separate facts from *a priori* and intuitive interpretations. Lorenz is, of course, entitled to use what language he chooses when he deals with his own observations—his geese can be treated as humans, and his humans as geese. But it is a different matter when he cites the presumed data of others, and where one has the right to assume the utmost critical caution if fact is not to become inextricably mingled with fiction. Who, for example, has seen "small apes . . . leaping after a tiger or a leopard"? And to how many readers does Lorenz address the sentence "anybody who has ever seen . . . the male chimpanzee defending his band or family with self-sacrificing courage"? Has this ever been seen? How, again, does Lorenz make a ruptured carotid artery fill the body-cavities with blood? That is curious anatomy indeed. And who was it who showed, and how, that the dog's inhibition against biting bitches is "chemically induced"? Are the "essential facts of biology" really easier to comprehend, as he claims, "than integral calculus or the computing of compound interest"? If they are, it must be a very simple and superficial kind of biology of which he is speaking.

The kind of doubt which this kind of writing conjures up is perhaps less serious than certain other shortcomings in Lorenz's formulations. We can applaud when he writes that the concept of instinct does not provide any explanation of the particular processes, such as reproduction, to which it may be applied. But is it less tautological, or more meaningful scientifically, to say "that all instinctive motor patterns possess their own spontaneity, their own action-specific production of endogenous stimulation whose quality is quite exactly calculated to meet the demand which is to be expected in the organism's normal environment"? What kind of explanation does Lorenz intend this circular proposition to convey, and where does it differ logically from the usual concept of instinct? As Skinner * has recently pointed out, it is equally misleading to assume that one can safely infer the "phylogenic contingencies" by which a given pattern of behaviour may have been transformed over thousands or even millions of years; or because the behaviour pattern appears "adaptive," decide what kind of evolutionary process was responsible for it. In so far as it conveys this impression Lorenz's book is, as Skinner implies, simply misleading. How, for example, can Lorenz blandly write that it is quite "certain" that the Indian pipe of peace "developed into a fixed ritual which became law for every Indian and prohibited aggression after pipe-smoking"—on the basis of a speculation that one of two angry Indian chiefs may once have forgotten his pipe, and was allowed a puff by his enemy in order to enjoy the "tension relieving catharsis of smoking"? On what foundations of historical knowledge does this "certainty" rest? Speculations such as these—and Lorenz indulges in many—may be fascinating, but they are not science. The

* Skinner, B. F., *Science*, 153, 1205 (1966).

complexities of human social and political behaviour cannot be explained on the basis of oversimplified homologies and analogies with highly selective aspects of animal behaviour.

Lorenz is the acknowledged father of what is now called ethology. If this is to become more of a science than it sometimes appears, its disciples, while acknowledging their debt to him, would be wise to be more rigorous than he usually is in showing where observation gives way to *a priori* interpretation, and how casual is differentiated from controlled observation. This, it is true, may lead to duller writing than that which we get from Konrad Lorenz himself. But in the end ethology will benefit less from his assurance, the assurance which allows him to write that he is "being far from presumptuous" in professing the conviction that "in the very near future not only scientists but the majority of tolerably intelligent people" will treat his views as "obvious and banal truth," than it will from "scientific humility," whose virtues one vainly expects Lorenz to extol in the chapter which he heads "On the Virtue of Scientific Humility." Ethology is hardly likely to prove an exception to that major lesson of science which warns that the beliefs of today are not necessarily those of tomorrow.

Territory and Aggression in Man:
A Look at Ardrey's *Territorial Imperative*

This book should be subtitled "An Autobiography of Primitive Thought." Ardrey's book proves his main point regarding continuity of behavior in modern man with lower animal forms: what remains a difficult task is to ascertain which ancestors are most responsible for this thought—planarian worms, lemurs, slime-molds, or the brash cock robin. If this appears vindictive, the reader is correct: I would prefer to have my time back. Actually, according to Ardrey's thesis regarding the instinctual basis of human behavior, the question has a sense of fairness in it. Initially, my reaction was that nobody had really understood Ardrey's aim—here was one of the best satires written—but further reading led unerringly to the conclusion that the author is indeed serious.

Nowhere in this book will one find a closely, tightly knit reasoned statement or hypothesis which interrelates a number of scattered variables such as territorial behavior, aggressiveness, amity, enmity, stimulation, security, identity, natural selection, and which could be tested for logical consistency or empirical support. Instead, in dramatic and scattered fashion the author parades forth a plethora of behavioral instincts (some his own invention), under the protective wrapper of "the new biology" (which alas, is denied

Reprinted with permission from the *Political Science Quarterly*, December 1967, Vol. LXXXII, No. 4, pp. 630–32. New material added by author, 1968.

to our children's education), and does little more than assert that anyone in disagreement with his view of man and his instincts is ignorant, a clinger to religion, a throwback to an older generation of non-informed biologists, a sycophant trying to rationalize his own instincts. In short, Ardrey has almost constructed a religion, very much along Freudian lines, where dissent or skepticism is explained by the theory itself. Perhaps this is fine drama—it is hardly science. When Ardrey says that this is a "personal inquiry" he is not exaggerating. Unfortunately, the "personal" aspects enter into the argument—we are constantly reminded about his personal acquaintances, drinking buddies, and the recent budding generation of baboon watchers, all brought to the reader's attention as authoritative—the possibility that many of this list of heroes very likely might disagree with Ardrey is never mentioned. In short, this is one of Ardrey's tactics. We learn of Ardrey's competence and professional background—he once lectured in anthropology in one of the booths at the Chicago World's Fair in the 1930's.

The methodology needs explanation. Ardrey starts by making a general assertion as if it were heretical, e.g., that man's behavior is a product of evolution. He expands this into a non-sequitur that man carries around some particular behavioral pattern from his ancestry. Next, Ardrey recounts the animal studies (it may be slime-molds, birds, or penguins) to prove that behavior, e.g., territorial defense, has an instinctual, innate basis. Next, one is warned that if he dissents and doesn't see the instinctual basis of human international behavior in these examples, he is guilty of not believing in evolution, and a sort of "see there, I told you so," mentality takes over—Ardrey feels he has proven his point. His strategy is to repeat this tactic again and again, going from the slime to the sublime until the brainwashing is hopefully communal. Nowhere does one find a single whit of evidence provided for human instincts: that is unnecessary according to Ardrey's methodology. We simply jump to collective farms, National Character, or International relationships to prove the innate basis of individual men's behavior. Associated with these tactics is the ever-occurring assertion that he is breaking new ground—that nowhere in his extensive notes has he ever found this approach used before. The phrase "Social Darwinism" never appears in this book. Too bad, for that is essentially the message of the book. Ardrey is uninformed if he thinks that there have never been attempts to reduce human group behavior to a few animal instincts. He is wrong if he believes that International bodies have never before been seen as organisms. Ardrey accepts group selection theory as proven, even though most biologists know that this is an area of considerable debate. There is misinformation about the ubiquity of primate territoriality, and many of the recent advances in the eufunctions of spacing behavior particularly in terms of disease resistance and adaptation are omitted.

It is worthwhile to go more deeply into this matter of tactics whereby one is branded anti-evolutionistic if he views the discontinuities between man and other animals of signal importance. Nowhere has this been better phrased than in Konrad Lorenz's article, "Ritualized Fighting," in *The Natural History of Aggression*.* Indeed, many parts of Ardrey's book rely on Lorenz's formulations, but in more dramatic and less careful ways. Lorenz notes:

> There cannot be any doubt, in the opinion of any biologically-minded scientist, that intraspecific aggression is, in Man, just as much of a spontaneous instinctive drive as in most other higher vertebrates. The beginning synthesis between the findings of ethology and psychoanalysis does not leave any doubt, either, that what . . . Freud called the "death drive" is nothing else but the miscarrying of this instinct which, in itself, is as indispensable for survival as any other.

Now, what about dissenters?

> However, it comes very hard to people not versed in biological thought to concede that Man, with a capital M, still does possess instincts in common with animals. That particular kind of pride which proverbially comes before a fall prevents men from understanding the workings of their own instincts, including that of aggression. As it is causal insight alone which can ever give us the power to influence chains of events and to direct them to our own ends, it is highly dangerous to assume the ostrich attitude in respect to the nature of human instincts. (p. 49)

* J. D. Carthy and F. J. Ebling (eds.), *The Natural History of Aggression*. New York: Academic Press, 1964.

Man, like any other animal, has evolved a repertoire of behavioral patterns under the exacting influence of natural selection. The notion of species-specific behavior, its ontogenesis and structural underpinnings need not require a cathection upon some list of instincts to explain human behavior. One does not have to search very far in the literature to find many "biologically-minded scientists" who do not feel that man's aggression is best compared with the "spontaneous instinctive drive as in most other higher vertebrates." One does not have far to go in the literature to discern a general displeasure with the proposition that any higher vertebrates have instincts. Names such as Lehrman, Schneirla, or Berkowitz do not appear in Ardrey's book, and the whole hoary question of innate patterns is assumed already solved.

This leads directly to another maddening shortcoming of this general holier-than-thou approach of the "true" biologically-minded scientist. One of the outstanding successes of the ethologist school has been the investigation and delineation of critical sign-stimuli, the cue functions of the environmental surround which figure in an adaptive sense in the animal's behavior, and which act to release certain sequences of motor action in the animal's interest, providing that the internal conditions are appropriate, whether it be in terms of self- or species preservation.

What are the critical sign stimuli for the human, which act to release stereotypical adaptive responses? What are the invariances of the cue functions in the human environment which help to release specific motor patterns built up through evolution by natural selection? Red feathers, blue gew gaws, green turf, butyric acid, white eye lids, the exposed neck, flashing white tails, etc., etc., have been identified for numerous animals. What are the critical sign stimuli which make up the human "Umwelt"? The question is not about human aggressive responses to stimuli. The sordid history of man attests well to the fantastic plurality of "stimuli" that can be cooked up to elicit aggression. How natural are they? Have the gentiles undergone a special process of evolution and natural selection so that they respond instinctively to some critical sign stimulus of Jewishness, and vice versa? To reduce the question to absurdity, would any "biologically-minded scientist" aver that each human symbol cluster that elicits aggressive responses was gained through natural selection just as the stickleback reacts to red, or certain bower birds to blue? Until the specific sign stimuli can be identified (as for one possible example, the smiling face and the human infant's reaction to it), the analogies to lower animals' species-specific patterns represent outrageous intellectual slighting, not ground-breaking. Skepticism about human instincts is not any attack on the animal nature of man, or an arrogant suggestion that man does not act according to natural and man-made laws. Such skepticism need not blind anyone to the possibility of innate dispositions in humankind to define certain environmental contexts as inimical to their interests, and to act aggressively toward these clusters. The object is not, as some social scientists have tended to do, to rid man of his biological heritage, or to deny that his psychobiological makeup is species-specific. Innate predispositions are not the same thing as instincts, a concept continually being amended to include more outside variables integrated with learning and internal physiological state.

Perhaps egoism and self-esteem are innate properties of the species man, which during ontogenetic development can go in different but limited directions depending on the cultural milieu in which various peoples thrive or cope. Hostility and aggression toward sources frustrating the attainment of particular cognitive definitions of the self can be biologically based and species-specific without recourse to the suggestions of Lorenz and Ardrey that such responses can best be understood by studying the birds, bees, and baboons. Human aggression is no less real, or without biological basis because it is acted out in extraordinary various ways, or that it responds to an almost infinite variety of physical and symbolic stimuli. The variety itself implicates the overriding importance of learning in different cultural contexts, the types of frustrations particular subcultures are most prone to suffer, and the vast mass of literature in the psychological (both experimental and social) and sociological journals is replete with numerous instances of cultural manipulation of aggression. The biological literature is no less prepared to offer Ardrey numerous examples of the importance of learning and the nature of cue functions in nonhuman animal aggression. Almost all of the examples used by Ardrey, and those from the major works of ethological research show a fairly clear-cut locking-in between discrete stimuli or environmental cues, action patterns, and adaptation to selected coterminous features of the environment. The peculiarly locking-in aspects for man have been replaced by plasticity welded into a species-specific pattern of ego structuring and maturation, the whole imbedded in a wide variety of symbolic environments. Animals other than man are interesting objects of study, and one cannot disclaim that the results of such have heuristic merit. For man, however, we need a species-specific theory which will not only account for aggression, but the total psychobiological matrix which has also been under natural selection, and has evolved during at least two million years of evolution. Human sentiment structures are varied and deep. Tears, laughter, sympathy, empathy, altruism, sacrifice, love, cooperation, prolonged deferment of gratification, each is a part of the human specificity. Their integration presupposes an evolutionary development far more complicated than the relatively simple key-lock framework of lower animals' behavior and evolution. To this reader it seems somewhat stupefying to reduce the reactions felt by many Americans after the bombing of Pearl Harbor to a set of simple territorial patterns of behavior. The question of "how many wars have been fought over women and how many over land (territory)" seems no more refined than popular drama requires.

There are some good points to this book. It is well-written—Ardrey can write—and the reader will appreciate the dramatist's skill, and will learn something about the behaviors of different animals (often fascinating), without having to read the dry, original scientific reports. That is, if he is willing to trust the selectiveness of Ardrey's perception and accuracy of reportage. The type is large, his wife's illustrations succinct and dramatic, and the book reads quickly—a distinct advantage for the reader. People with various prejudices for and against Italians, Jews, Black South Africans, free enterprise, and collective farms, will be treated to the end products of Ardrey's thought processes. The Italians are organized like the Lemurs. Black South Africans now prospering under the largesse of Apartheid policies will (85%) rise up in indignant wrath and defense of their White benefactors should any liberation attempts be made on the part of their brothers in the rest of Africa. In short, this book is an apology and rationalization for Imperialism, Pax

Americana, Laissez Faire, Social Darwinism, and that greatest of all evolutionary developments, Capitalism. Of course, there is a drawback which Ardrey takes pain to elaborate upon. Those intruded upon gain a certain energy from the fact that the territory is theirs, so intruders must take into account the likely intensity of reaction to their intrusion. (This energy gain is based on numerous animal studies in which the defender usually drives the intruder back into its own territory—never mind what the nature of the stimuli might be for the intruder.) This framework will surely interest those who have studied the history of the Third Reich. One thing Ardrey does not explain is why, when a Nation (organism?) has ample territory, abundance of food, resources, stimulation, security, it nevertheless wants more and more. Territorial instincts, energy gains and losses, slime molds, noyaus, bower birds, identity, stimulation, amity-enmity-hazard, are hardly necessary, and one fails to see how they offer any richer understanding than simple *greed* and *stupidity*.

In the final chapter, the Three Faces of Janus, one has the distinct impression that at last Ardrey has raised the really important issues, that somewhere in all this anthropomorphizing and animalizing of man's behavior, there are truths, and that Ardrey is on to something very important. Perhaps his next book will do it. This one fails and in a maddening, glib way.

It is only fitting to close this review with a quote from Ardrey: "Men, unlike mockingbirds, have the capacity for systematic self-delusion."

OMER C. STEWART

Lorenz/Margolin on the Ute

My long association and interest in the Ute Indians * compel me to call attention to the completely false picture of these people which has appeared in the popular book, *On Aggression,* by Konrad Lorenz. On pages 244-45, Lorenz writes:

> Sydney Margolin, in Denver, Colorado, made very exact psycho-analytical and psycho-sociological studies on Prairie Indians, particularly the Utes, and showed that these people suffer greatly from an excess of aggression drive which, under the ordered conditions of present-day North American Indian reservations, they are unable to discharge. It is Margolin's opinion that during the comparatively few centuries when Prairie Indians led a wild life consisting almost entirely of war and raids, there must have been an extreme selection pressure at work, breeding extreme aggressiveness. That this produced changes in the hereditary pattern in such a short time is quite possible. Domestic animals can be

* My study of the Ute began in 1930 and has continued to the present time. My research has been concerned with their ancient ethnology, their history, and their adjustment to modern life. I have had a special interest in their religion and have been a participant observer in the ceremonies of the Ute Sun Dance and the Native American Church (Peyote religion). From 1959 to 1964, I was co-director of an interdisciplinary project, with psychologists and sociologists, financed by a grant from the National Institute of Mental Health, of the U.S. Dept. of Health, Education, and Welfare (Project No. 3M-9556), which included collecting and analyzing all available records of the past history of the Ute of Colorado, as well as making an exhaustive study of their present values and behavior. Our first major publication, by Richard Jessor *et al.,* is in press.

changed just as quickly by purposeful selection. Margolin's assumption is supported by the fact that Ute Indians now growing up under completely different educational influences suffer in exactly the same way as the older members of their tribe who grew up under the educational system of their own culture; moreover, the pathological symptoms under discussion are seen only in those Prairie Indians whose tribes were subjected to the selection process described.

Ute Indians suffer more frequently from neurosis than any other human group, and again and again Margolin found that the cause of the trouble was undischarged aggression. Many of these Indians feel and describe themselves as ill, and when asked what is the matter with them they can only say, "I am a Ute!" Violence toward people not of their tribe, and even manslaughter, belong to the order of the day, but attacks on members of the tribe are extremely rare, for they are prevented by a taboo the severity of which it is easy to understand, considering the early history of the Utes: a tribe constantly at war with neighboring Indians and, later on, with the white man, must avoid at all costs fights between its own members. Anyone killing a member of the tribe is compelled by strict tradition to commit suicide. This commandment was obeyed even by a Ute policeman who had shot a member of his tribe in self-defense while trying to arrest him. The offender, while under the influence of drink, had stabbed his father in the femoral artery, causing him to bleed to death. When the policeman was ordered by his sergeant to arrest the man for manslaughter—it was obviously not murder—he protested, saying that the man would want to die since he was bound by tradition to commit suicide and would do so by resisting arrest and forcing the policeman to shoot him. He, the policeman, would then have to commit suicide himself. The more than shortsighted sergeant stuck to his order, and the tragedy took place exactly as predicted. This and other of Margolin's records read like Greek tragedies: an inexorable fate forces crime upon people and then compels them to expiate voluntarily their involuntarily acquired guilt.

It is objectively convincing, indeed it is proof of the correctness of Margolin's interpretation of the behavior of Ute Indians, that these people are particularly susceptible to accidents. It has been proved that accident-proneness may result from repressed aggression, and in these Utes the rate of motor accidents exceeds that of any other car-driving human group. Anybody who has ever driven a fast car when really angry knows—in so far as he is capable of self-observation in this condition—what strong inclination there is to self-destructive behavior in a situation like this. Here even the expression "death wish" seems apt.

Since Lorenz gives no bibliography on Margolin and Margolin seems not to have published his work on the Ute, I take it Lorenz's information about the Ute came from Margolin in private conversation or lecture. Margolin has lectured on the Ute, and having heard two of his lectures, I believe he would subscribe to the views attributed to him by Lorenz.

It is always disconcerting when two people, both studying the same subject at the same time, come up with entirely different conclusions, and to be one of them. One would expect some difference, of course, stemming from a psychoanalytical, Freudian approach, on the one hand, and an objective, historical-anthropological approach such as I use, on the other.* However, I disagree with Margolin's facts, as well as his conclusions, and I object to the looseness of his language regarding anthropological facts. For instance, the Ute Indians are not Prairie Indians, but are Mountain and Great Basin Indians.

Furthermore, Plains and Prairie Indian ethnohistory does not reveal that those people "led a wild life consisting almost entirely of war and raids." They had war and they did raid, but their history was not of such war and raiding to make them unique among social groups. The Ute Indians were early horsemen and hunted buffalo on the High Plains. While there, they were prepared to fight or run, and they always returned to the Rocky Mountains and maintained their homes there. In early historic times, they were often referred to as the "Swiss" Indians.

The implication that the Ute were a violent people, addicted to war, is not borne out by historic facts. With the early Spanish settlers, the Utes were primarily friendly traders; later, they had amicable relations with Americans. In 1776, the Utes guided Escalante

---

* See my paper, "Need To Popularize Basic Concepts." I realize that anthropology today is being fertilized by many disciplines, including psychoanalysis, and although this is certainly beneficial, anthropologists should not lose sight of basic anthropological concepts.

through their territory; in 1806, they guided Pike. They were collaborators with the American trappers following the Louisiana Purchase and the explorations of Lewis and Clark. During the Civil War, they served as paid scouts and allies of the U.S. Army in wars against plains tribes and the Navaho, yet immediately after these skirmishes, they made visits to the same tribes and welcomed return visits. The Utes collaborated with the U.S. government in nearly every way and became aggressive only under extreme provocation, such as when betrayed by Agent Meeker and threatened by an unwarranted armed invasion of their reservation in 1879.

The Utes not only were not addicted to unusual "violence toward people not of their tribe," but they did not have a rule that "anyone killing a member of the tribe is compelled by strict tradition to commit suicide." I have known personally four Utes who killed fellow Utes; none committed suicide. One, living on the Southern Ute Reservation in 1964, was convicted of murdering his uncle who was a policeman. He had served time in a Federal Prison and was home on parole. A similar case was a Ute who had killed his wife. Suicides and attempted suicides among the Ute have not been murderers of fellow tribesmen.

Like most other American Indians, the Ute have been victims of alcohol and under its influence have committed many criminal acts and have been careless with their own lives and the lives of others. But this has been true of the tribes of the Atlantic Coast states, the Chippewa of the Great Lakes, the Northwest Coast fishing Indians, etc. All of these Indians, like the Utes, are known far and wide for their accidents while under the influence of alcohol. The problem of the American Indians' excessive use of alcohol is a very real problem, but is it not unique to one tribe, the Ute, and there appears to be no justification to make a separate explanation of Ute or Prairie Indian alcoholism as resulting from repressed aggression. Ute accident rate is high because excessive use of alcohol is high.

Interested in what others closely associated with the Ute thought of Margolin's description of the Ute as reported in Lorenz's book, I duplicated the passages quoted at the beginning of this paper and sent them to three people who have had many close associations with the Ute: Elbert J. Floyd, former extension agent and superin-

tendent to the Ute, now living near the Ute Reservation in retire-
ment from the Bureau of Indian Affairs and closely associated with
the Ute since 1919; John R. (Bob) White, employed by the Ute
Indians as "information officer," from 1954 to 1961, then hired as
assistant to the superintendent of the Consolidated Ute Agency,
Colorado, until 1963, since then associated with other tribes; and
Arthur L. Warner, M.D., M.P.H. Medical Director, San Juan Basin
Health Unit, 1958–1965. I asked them to read the passage and then
sign the following statement with me, if they cared to do so:

> The undersigned have read pages 244–245 of the book, *On Ag-
> gression.* "It is erroneous to say that Utes have killed or seek to
> kill non-Utes while avoiding attacks on fellow Utes. Utes have
> murdered members of their own tribe as frequently as they have
> killed non-whites in the last century. Utes who have committed
> suicides were not Ute murderers. In excessive use of alcohol the
> Ute are like other Indians. Ute accident rate does not exceed that
> of other heavy drinking groups."

All three signed this statement. In addition, Dr. Warner wrote:
"I have studied vital statistics and social behavior of the Utes, and I
am thoroughly acquainted with their patterns of injury, suicide,
and death." Mr. Floyd wrote, in part, "I am personally familiar
with a case where a Ute Mountain Ute policeman shot and killed a
fellow Ute while attempting an arrest; however, the policeman did
not commit suicide." Mr. White added, "The high rate of Indian
auto accidents has been a matter of concern of tribal governments,
the Bureau, and the Public Health Service for some time. But this
situation is by no means confined to the Utes. It applies to almost
every Indian tribe. The statement on page 245 that 'anyone killing
a member of the tribe is compelled by strict tradition to commit
suicide' certainly came as news to me. The Ute Mountain suicide
rate was a matter of some concern at one time, and still may be, but
I cannot recall any suicide linked to a previous killing."

Margolin's statements of fact which are subject to testing concerning the Ute Indians are simply not correct. Others are questionable. Has Margolin the statistics to substantiate the claim that
"Ute Indians suffer more frequently from neurosis than any other
human group"? As a group, the Ute Indians seem to differ slightly
from other people in a number of ways. These differences are not

great, or sensational, or sweeping. They are, however, based on painstakingly collected facts, established by psychologists and sociologists, as well as anthropologists, using carefully prepared interview guides, selected samples, and statistical analysis. These are contained in the reports of the Tri-ethnic project published or in press under the names of Richard Jessor, Robert Hanson, and Theodore Graves.

Finally, the peyote religion of the Ute is a significant refutation of the Lorenz-Margolin thesis. The Ute appear to have been receptive to peyote as early as 1900, according to Mooney, who reported their participation in the peyote religion with the Jicarilla Apache. Their interest grew by means of visits to Taos and Oklahoma until the cult was firmly established, especially on the Ute Mountain Ute Reservation in south-western Colorado, where it flourished from 1916 on. The peyote religion is a syncretistic cult, incorporating ancient Indian and modern Christian elements. The Christian theology of love, charity, and forgiveness has been added to the ancient Indian ritual and aboriginal desire to acquire personal power through individual visions. Peyotism has taught a program of accommodation for over 50 years and the peyote religion has succeeded in giving Indians pride in their native culture while adjusting to the dominant civilization of the whites.

ANNOTATED BIBLIOGRAPHY

Aberle, David F. and Stewart, Omer C. 1967. *Navaho and Ute Peyotism: A Chronological and Distributional Study.*
University of Colorado Studies—Series in Anthropology: No. 6, 129 pages.
This study documents the long-standing intimate relationship which has existed between Ute and Navajo Indians, in spite of the wars between them before 1870. The Navaho learned peyotism from the Ute during years of mutual participation in ceremonies, often directed by peyote priests from other tribes.

Bolton, Herbert E., ed. 1950: Pageant in the Wilderness, *Utah Historical Quarterly*, XVIII.
Translation of the journal of Father Escalante, who led a small expedition for months in 1776 through the Ute Indian country in what is now the states of Colorado and Utah. His observations

leave no doubt that the Ute then had primarily a Great Basin culture, notwithstanding the fact that the easternmost groups had horses and hunted from time to time upon the High Plains immediately east of the Rocky Mountains.

Rockwell, Wilson. 1956. *The Utes: a Forgotten People*. Denver, The Sage Press. Historical account of the friendly relationship between Ute Indians and white Americans.

Slotkin, J. S. 1956. *The Peyote Religion: a Study in Indian-White Relations*. Glencoe, Illinois: The Free Press.

In a brilliant analytic study of the theology and history of peyotism, Slotkin found: "The peyote religion was nativistic but not militant. Culturally, it permitted the Indians to achieve a cultural organization in which they took pride. Socially, it provided a supernatural means of accommodation to the existing domination-subordination relation."

Stewart, Omer C. 1942. *Culture Elements Distribution: XVIII, Ute, Southern Paiute*. University of California—Anthropological records. 6:231–380.

A recording, in chart form and notes, of the basic elements of Ute and Southern Paiute culture traits, as remembered by many of the oldest members of these tribes in 1937 and 1938, in both Utah and Colorado.

—— 1948. *Ute Peyotism*. University of Colorado Studies—Series in Anthropology, No. 1, 42 pages.

A description of the peyote ceremony of the Ute, based on participation in the religious cult on Unitah Reservation, Utah, and the Ute Mountain Ute Reservation, Colorado. About 90 per cent of the Ute Mountain Ute are active peyotists. Peyotism is a minority religion on the other Ute reservations.

—— 1952. "Southern Ute Indians Adjustment to Modern Living," *Acculturation in the Americas: Selected papers from the XXIXth International Congress of Americanists (New York, 1949)*. University of Chicago Press, pp. 80–88.

This is a preliminary report of reasearch in Colorado, initiated in 1948, and continuing.

—— 1964. "Questions Regarding American Indian Criminality," *Human Organization*, vol. 23, No. 1, Spring, 1964, pp. 61–66.

Nation-wide comparative study of Indian difficulties with the law, which usually involved an excessive use of alcohol.

—— 1964. "The Need To Popularize Basic Concepts," *Current Anthropology*, vol. 5, no. 5, pp. 431, 442.

Anthropologists should return frequently to teach the concept that culture is entirely invented by man and is transmitted by learning.

—— 1966. "Ute Indians: Before and After White Contact." *Utah Historical Quarterly,* vol. 34, No. 1, (Winter 1966) pp. 38–61.

A short analysis of Ute culture which reveals its basic Great Basin character. This paper contains also a review of the long record of friendly relations betweeen the Ute and the U.S. government.

JOHN BEATTY

Taking Issue with Lorenz on the Ute

In his book, *On Aggression,* K. Lorenz, basing his statements on field work done by Sydney Margolin, states that the Ute have been genetically selected for aggression by the nature of their war-oriented culture. Lorenz says that Margolin ". . . made very exact psychoanalytical and psycho-sociological studies on Prairie Indians, particularly the Utes, and showed that these people suffer greatly from an excess of aggression drive, which under the ordered conditions of present day North American Indian reservations, they are unable to discharge." (Lorenz, 1966, p. 244)

Margolin reports, according to Lorenz (*op. cit.,* p. 244), that the Prairie Indians led a "wild life consisting almost entirely of war and raids." He says that this type of life went on for several centuries. "Extreme selection pressure" must have been at work "breeding extreme aggressiveness" (*op. cit.,* p. 244). Lorenz also states that "Violence toward people not of their tribe and even manslaughter belong to the order of the day . . ."

The Ute are not a Prairie tribe as Lorenz and Margolin state. They are classified as a Basin Indian tribe (Murdock, 1960). Despite the several hundred mile geographic displacement, it is important to discuss the several assumptions, hypotheses and theoretical concepts which underlie the statements made by Lorenz and Mar-

The stimulus for this paper was produced by a series of discussions with Dr. Ethel Tobach.

golin. One of these is Lorenz's theory that aggression is in fact genetically programmed and therefore may be inbred. The other assumptions involve the Ute themselves. This paper will not attempt to deal with the theoretical basis for Lorenz's use of Margolin's data. It will, however, show that Margolin's Ute material as cited is erroneous; and that the Ute culture cannot be used to substantiate the dubious idea that aggression may be genetically controlled.

Lorenz states that Margolin believes that "extreme selection pressure" worked at "breeding extreme aggressiveness." (*op. cit.,* p. 244). To breed for a trait would require a closed population. In order to inbreed one must choose selectively the mating partners for the desired trait. If exogamous genetic material is introduced to a population gene pool, neither inbreeding nor trait selection occurs. In order to maintain a gene pool, selectively bred for aggressive behavior, one of two marrying patterns would have to be followed: (1) a Ute could marry another Ute; (2) a Ute could marry a member of a group which was also selectively bred for aggression. According to Lorenz, "The pathological symptoms under discussion are seen only in those Prairie Indians whose tribes were subjected to the selection processes described" (*op. cit.,* p. 244).

To be consistent with Margolin's scheme, one must assume that only those who were aggressive would be permitted to mate. To accomplish this, fulfillment of a criterion of aggressivity through participation in warfare or other aggressive behavior would have to have been a prerequisite to marriage.

These assumptions are not supportable. Insofar as inbreeding is concerned, we find that the Ute marital patterns are not solely Ute-Ute or Ute-prairie-tribe marriages. As a matter of fact, the Ute engaged in some warfare, basically raids, which were carried out primarily for the purpose of women stealing (Driver, 1961, p. 358). These raids were made on the non-Prairie Pueblos (Driver, 1961, p. 366). The Pueblos have long been described as non-aggressive. Ruth Benedict (1934) contrasts their peaceable nature with that of other Indian groups, pointing out their lack of tolerance of violence (1934, p. 114). They are believers in moderation (*op. cit.,* p. 93), and will have nothing to do with disruptive individual experience (*op. cit.,* p. 93).

Rockwell (1956, p. 49) states that in addition to out-marriages with the Pueblo tribes, the Ute also married the non-Prairie Bannock and Snake Indians living to the West. This would further invalidate the conclusion of Lorenz and Margolin, since it was stated that only Prairie tribes "were subjected to the selection pressures described." (Lorenz 1963, p. 244) Since the Bannock and Snake or Pueblo Indians do not qualify for the "selection pressures," we must assume that they are not aggressive peoples and are, therefore, introducing genetically different material into the Ute gene pool.

The basis for the choice of marriage partners among the Ute is not authoritatively presented in the literature. Parkhill (1962, p. 50) says that to enter manhood, a test involving the exhibition of hunting skills must be passed. After this the man is an eligible marriage partner. It should be noted that Lorenz does not consider hunting to be a form of aggression.

Lorenz (1963, p. ix) only considers aggression to be "the fighting instinct in beast and man *against* members of the same species." He considers the Ute aggressive because of their supposed "wild life consisting of war and raids," and that ". . . violence . . . and even manslaughter belong to the order of the day" (*op. cit.*, p. 244). However, the Annual Reports of the Commissioner of Indian Affairs (from 1884 on) indicate that the most common crime is drunkenness, that murder occurs only rarely and that there are few recordings of non-Utes murdered by Utes, or Utes murdered by Utes. Most murders are of Utes by non-Utes (i.e., whites and neighboring tribes). Suicides occur but seem unrelated to the intra-Ute murder rate. It is relevant to note that Hrdlička observed that a suicide in 1904 was the first recorded suicide among the southern Ute and that at that time it was the only one in memory (Hrdlička, 1908, p. 171). There is no mention of a related Ute-Ute murder. Lorenz, however, points out that "Anyone killing a member of the tribe is compelled by strict tradition to commit suicide" (*op. cit.*, p. 245).

The last piece of evidence which indicates that the Ute are not as aggressive and war-loving as Margolin and Lorenz would have us believe, comes from the text of a speech made by a Ute at the opening of the Ute Bear Dance, which had been observed by V. Z. Reed in 1896 (Reed, 1896, p. 272). In this speech, the Ute states that ". . . times have been good . . . we have had no wars . . ."

Lorenz also makes two questionable assumptions about the nature of warfare as a cultural institution. The first is that warfare is fundamentally aggressive behavior, and the second, that repressed aggression is the only factor which could be responsible for the contemporary behavior of the Ute.

Although the Ute are not true Plains Indians, their warfare pattern is similar to those of the Plains tribes. The Plains Indian warfare is highly ritualized (cf. Lorenz, 1963, p. 280), and based on raids (Driver, 1961, p. 359). Most common reasons given for warfare are women stealing and economic purposes, e.g., horse stealing (Driver, 1961, p. 359). In the actual encounters, killing and scalping occurred, but were not of paramount importance. According to Grinnell (1910, p. 296) it was the counting of coup that occupied the prime position of honor. Grinnell says (1910, p. 297), "Neither the killing nor the scalping was regarded as an especially creditable act. The chief applause was won by the man who could first touch the fallen enemy. In Indian estimation the bravest act that could be performed was to count coup on—to touch or strike—a living unhurt man and to leave him alive, and this was frequently done."

Margolin supports his hypothesis about repressed aggression by reporting that the Ute are more accident prone than "any other car driving group" (Lorenz, 1963, p. 245). The data to support such a statement are not given, nor is it clear how repressed aggression was concluded to be the main factor in car accidents. Considering the poverty of most American Indian groups the automobiles that the Ute are able to afford may be the more relevant factor in the analysis of the causes of accidents.

Lorenz discusses the implication of repressed aggression further in his views on neurosis. "Ute Indians suffer more frequently from neurosis than any other human group" (Lorenz, 1963, p. 244). This observation by Lorenz, without substantiating data is far-fetched and scientifically of little merit, as cross cultural considerations of mental illness are problematical and difficult at best. As Barnouw points out (1963, p. 362), "Another difficulty in making cross-cultural comparisons, is that what seems normal and acceptable behavior in one society may be regarded as abnormal and wrong in another. Ruth Benedict drew attention to this problem, pointing out that in many parts of the world, vision and trance behavior are not only considered normal, but may carry prestige." Further, Lorenz's assertion is meaningless in view of the lack of valid and reliable information available on the demography of neurosis.

Although the Ute may be neurotic by Western standards, as are most acculturating groups (Barnouw, 1963, p. 381), there is no published evidence to show that the "neurosis" of the Ute is due specifically to repressed aggression. At the least, one must wait for the publication of Margolin's studies. On the basis of our current knowledge of the causes of neurosis, it is equally valid to ascribe the condition where it exists in the Ute to general deprivation and despair.

BIBLIOGRAPHY

Barnouw, Victor. 1963. *Culture and Personality*. Dorsey Press Inc. Homewood, Ill.

Benedict, Ruth. 1934. *Patterns of Culture*. Mentor Books-New American Library, New York.

Driver, Harold. 1961. *Indians of North America*. University of Chicago Press, Chicago, Ill.

Grinnell, George B. 1910. "Coup and Scalp Among the Plains Indians," *American Anthropologist*, 12: 296–310.

Hrdlička, A. 1908. *Physiological and Medical Observation Among the Indians of Southwestern United States and Northern Mexico*, Bulletin of the Bureau of American Ethnology, 34, Washington, D.C.

Lorenz, Konrad. 1963. *On Aggression*. Harcourt Brace and World Inc., New York.

Murdock, George Peter. 1960. *Ethnographic Bibliography of North America*. 3rd Edition, Human Relations Area File, New Haven.

Parkhill, Forbes. 1962. *Last of the Indian Wars*. Crowell-Collier, New York.

Reed, V. Z. 1896. "The Ute Bear Dance," *American Anthropologist*, 9: 237–44.

Rockwell, Wilson. 1956. *Utes: A Forgotten People*. A. Swallow, Denver, Colorado.

United States—Office of Indian Affairs. 1884– *Annual Report of the Commissioner of Indian Affairs*. Government Printing Office, Washington, D.C.

MARSHALL D. SAHLINS

African Nemesis: An Off-Broadway Review

Foreword

Robert Ardrey, the author of *African Genesis,* is a playwright. But he's a thinking man's playwright. He has conducted, as he puts it, a personal investigation into the animal origins and animal nature of man. The investigation focuses on the social behavior of subhuman primates and other vertebrates—most notably, birds—and on the South African "man-ape" (Australopithecine) materials uncovered by Raymond Dart and his co-workers. Ardrey claims to have discovered not merely the true underlying nature of man, but a large "unwitting combine" of influential scientists who refuse to acknowledge the evidences of this true nature. The true nature is made up of certain "cultural instincts" developed in the course of animal evolution and genetically transmitted in the human line. Most of the instincts are bad, and they are responsible for great troubles of the modern world. The combine, intellectually committed to the "romantic fallacy" that man is basically noble, unique among animals, and governed not so much by his animal nature as by his cultural circumstances, will not see this. So Ardrey has taken it upon himself to present the case to the public. He makes out his discovery to be a revolutionary doctrine, and with great flourish and

From *The Kroeber Anthropological Society Papers,* No. 30, Spring 1964, pp. 83–100. Reprinted by permission.

considerable flair lets fly many barbs in the general direction of the "phalanx of modern thought" and the bastions of "scientific orthodoxy."

However different the subject, the book then belongs in the popular Kon Tiki genre. It's agin the interests. It portrays a theory that sounds sensible, but which, for fuddy-duddy reasons, the professors-that-be generally ignore. Right away, Ardrey is an underdog. And to add to the appeal: simply by reading the book approvingly anyone can demonstrate that he is the intellectual equal—indeed, the superior of the so-called scholars.

Obviously, it becomes difficult to enter the lists against Ardrey. Who wants to be accused of being a counter-revolutionary? Who *is* a counter-revolutionary? What an improbable position for an anthropological critic. To admit to intellectual conservatism is contrary to the spirit of any science, and not the least so to anthropology. In this context of conspiratorial allegation, how can an anthropologist convey the impression that the theory seems to him unsound? Well, if Ardrey, a dramatist, can pen a book about anthropology, an anthropologist can write his review in play form. That is what I have done.

The play speaks for itself. *Insofar as it speaks well it is because I have woven into it many of Ardrey's felicitous phrases.* It is only necessary to mention that the bracketed page numbers refer to some of Ardrey's more unusual statements, and the dénouement of the drama is not Ardrey's book but my hope. So now your humble patience pray, gently to hear, kindly to judge:

Cast of Characters

ROBERT ARDENT: Former dramatist. Now leader of a revolutionary movement to reveal the true animal nature of man.

EVE ARDENT: His wife.

RAYMOND BLUNT: Anatomist-paleontologist. Discoverer of Australopithecus, the nearest ancestor of man.

DR. L. FAUCET: Noted anthropologist. Discoverer of the early hominid Zinjanthropus—under hazardous conditions due to the menace of prides of black-maned lions.

MARY FAUCET: His wife, the real discoverer of Zinjanthropus.

ANYONE: Almost everyone.

KUNG: A Bushman shaman. (Only we know his real name.)

MR. SHAPIRO: A Mr. Shapiro.

Any resemblance between the characters of this play and persons living or dead is purely incidental.

PROLOGUE

Ardent and Eve on opposite ends of stage front.

ARDENT. Give order that these bodies
High on a stage be placed to view;
And let me speak to the yet unknowing world
How these things came about. So shall you hear
Of carnal, bloody, and unnatural acts;
Of accidental judgments, casual slaughters;
Of deaths put on by cunning and forced cause;

EVE (*an interjected aside*). And, in this upshot, purposes mistook
Fall'n on the inventors' heads—

ARDENT. All this can I truly deliver.

ACT I

A cave near Johannesburg, late afternoon. A table and chair rear center with typewriter on table. A pile of firewood front center, about eight feet in front of table. Cave mouth, R; cave recess, L. Ardent, standing on table, addressing Blunt, the Faucets, Eve and Anyone. Mary Faucet carrying large rifle.

ARDENT (*dramatically*). A specter is haunting Europe—the million-year-old specter of a killer ape whose home was this very cave, the specter of man's carnivorous ancestor . . . his own murderous specter. All the powers of orthodox science, all the orthodox producers and consumers of the romantic fallacy, have entered into a holy alliance to exorcise this specter: Marx and Freud, Rousseau and Jefferson, the frightened anthropologists and their namby committed publics, the whole troop of howling monkeys that is man won't look in the goddam river of time to see reflected there their own hideous visage. (*Mocking*) Oh what a piece of work is man, they say: how noble in reason, in form and moving how express and admirable, in action how like an angel! The beauty of the world! The paragon of animals! (*Hardens*) Well, that is what he is, the paragon of animals: base to the core in instinct, in form and moving how like the beast of prey, in national action the consummate primate defending to a fool's death all the territory he can grab from others, the beauty of the mushroom cloud! Blunt, Faucet, Anyone—what is to be done? Murder will out, you thought, Blunt. Well you were wrong. So you cheerfully went up to the Livingstone conference to lay before the northern scientists the fossilized evidence from this cave. You put out in plain boxes the stupendous remnants of hominid carnage strewn here by our brutal Australopithecine father. Well, they ignored you! They took refuge behind the laughing hyena—hyenas did it, they said (*laughs bitterly*). And you, Faucet, you and Mary fighting off black-maned lions to dig in Tanganyika, to dig up the truth. I tell you this: they won't listen! Your specialist voices in obscure specialist journals have no echoes—even when you can get your stuff published. And they censor you. And they drown you in the milksop tears of the orthodox romantic prejudice. (*Exhorts*) I tell you this: you need drama! You need someone to put it all together, to forge a knife of prose that will rip the reactionary academics from groin to gorge. You need me! And we together will make our revolutionary truth known. Comrades, we are privy to a revolution in knowledge about man, about what he really is. South African workers in the caverns of man's origins, unite! Man has nothing to lose but the chains of his romantic illusion. Let us make him free with the truth. Let us break through the counter-revolutionary phalanx with a manifesto! And let us write it here—write here, right now! (*Anticlimax*) I have a publisher lined up—and catch this title, African Nemesis. (*Comes down from the table.*)

ANYONE. Is Marx an enemy of the revolution? A counter-revolutionary?

ARDENT. Private property is an animal instinct, a territorial compulsion put into the genes of man a hundred million years before he was born. (*Contempt*) But to the romantics, man is a noble fellow. Circumstances, they say, brought him to this end. A unique fellow, they say, with a soul, or a will, or a culture. I say . . . when Blunt found that bashed-in Australopithecine jaw, it said, said across millions of years of bloody history: man is a jabberwocky, a walkie-talkie, talking to disguise the fact that his talk means nothing. Man is an animal with the soul of a murderous, proprietary, status-seeking, in-group loving predator! Ah, we have found the jaws that bite. Next to this, all else is talk. The instincts must burst through. They are the true legacy of a man. He owns them. They own him.

ANYONE. I'm with you. Marx, fancy that. The history of all hitherto existing society is the animal history of animal struggles. Fancy that.

ARDENT (*motions Eve to table. She sits before typewriter. She types through scene, especially when Ardent speaks*). Light the fire for Eve to type by. Eve, you catch the spirit of the thing. I'll fix it up later.

FAUCET (*lighting fire, laughs good-humoredly*). Good job for the revolution that only man can make fire. (*Ardent glares at him and he stops laughing.*)

ANYONE. Can I put out the fire when we're done?

BLUNT. No me, me—

FAUCET. I made it, and I—

ARDENT. Stop this Freudian romanticism. We'll all do it, all four of us. We'll take different sides. But let's go back to the *real* beginning, the animal beginning, the hundreds-of-million-years old vertebrate beginning. Territory first, love of possession. Fish have it, birds have it, monkeys in the trees have it (Cole Porter 1938:2). It's in the genetic structure. The instinct to possess, the drive to gain, maintain and defend the exclusive right to a piece of territory. Man's cultural instinct for *Lebensraum*. Small hope for any United Nations that won't recognize that. It's the basic condition of war, of crime, of the fact that humans have a general reluctance to love their neighbors. Every man his own. Every tribe, every nation in territorial strife. An umbilical bondage to a piece of ground that decrees xenophobic hatred of the others of his kind. Got that, Eve? (*Listens.*) What's that? A scuffling in front of the cave. (*Sounds alarm.*) Counter-revolutionary scientific orthodox spies! Quiet everyone!

BLUNT. Ardent, I think you're getting a little paranoid.

ARDENT. In a world of man anything else would be insanity. Don't you ever have the feeling, Blunt, that paranoids are after you?

BLUNT. Don't worry, Ardent. I wrote up the report on this cave—no one could possibly find it.

FAUCET (*moves toward front of cave, R., startled, runs L. across stage and exit L., screaming in terror*). It's a pride of black maned lions! Run for your lives!

Mary Faucet advances boldly to cave mouth and fires high-powered rifle twice.

ARDENT (*emerging from behind table*). Get them, Mary old girl?

MARY. Got five lionesses and two cubs. I missed the male, though . . . he ran like hell.

ARDENT. It's hot in here. (*Removes shirt. Begins to pace around fire, with tempo of pacing gradually increasing through scene.*) *Faucet returns from stage left, dragging with him Kung, stone chisel and crude paint brushes in hand.*

FAUCET. Here's your counter-revolutionary, Ardent. He was painting a gazelle(schaft) back there on the walls of the cave. Human all right, but is it art?

ARDENT (*to Kung*). What are you doing here?

KUNG. Hunting.

ARDENT. The hell you are, you're painting an animal back there.

KUNG. Someone has to do the hunting.

BLUNT. He means he's searching out game by imitative magic.

ARDENT. Why don't you hunt like a man?

KUNG. I enjoy it . `.` . the arrow in the running beast, the red blood, the veldt. It *is* hunting. Besides I'm not very good at stalking. So I do the hunting. People give me some of the game sometimes.

ARDENT. Bushman, aren't you? You do this for band belong-you, people belong-you? Make-um magic?

KUNG. Sometimes for my band. But now I'm hunting for all the bands around here. Boys' initiation ceremony coming up. All the boys of all the bands and their people are coming in next week. We need a lot of game in our land to feed everyone. Big time. Good time.

ANYONE. What's your name, Bushman?

No answer.

ARDENT. C'mon, tell us name belong-you.

No answer.

BLUNT. He probably thinks you're going to take his name. He won't tell it to you. You might do something with his name, and he'll suffer.

ARDENT (*circling fire faster*). Leave him alone. A harmless people, and they suffer from it. . . Let's go on with the manifesto. Where were we? . . . territory, property . . . yes and next . . . Dominance! (*Excited again.*) The status-seeker. Man's unquenchable thirst for rank. An end in itself too; make no mistake on that. A drive, a need, a compulsion to dominate that continues on whether it's useful or useless. A basic desire for center stage. Try—

FAUCET. But—

ARDENT (*ignores interruption*)—to build an equalitarian society of men. Ha! Catch a falling star. How romantic. How delightful. Ha! Bushman, you got-em leader?

KUNG. We mostly listen to Tomu. We like him: a good man. Talks well. Generous to a fault. It's sometimes up to me, though. I mean if Tomu doesn't act right, we shamans see that he does. We know his real name, see. But no doubt you're right. Tomu must want badly to be the leader. Else why should he be so good?

Faucet begins to follow Ardent around fire. After a while he takes off his shirt and carries it. Pen, matches, cigarettes and other things periodically drop out of his shirt pocket. He reaches for them but often misses as he scurries to keep up with Ardent. Mary Faucet falls in after Faucet, picks up what he drops. Thus the two of them are stooping every once and a while as the dance goes on around the fire.

FAUCET. But listen, this rugged individualism I can understand. Yet there is some cooperation, you know.

ARDENT. Man is truly a social species, although when I say man here I don't embrace women (Linton 1932; after J. Miller 1698). Baboons too, and lots of lesser mammals. Necessary for survival, protection. Society is the animal's best friend, his defense, so sometimes he plays down his personal desires for the group. It's a kind of primal morality, a development of a double standard. Amity of the in-group, enmity toward the other groups. But listen to me, and don't get me wrong: it's a love born of hate, hate and fear of the outside. It multiplies hate by the factor of society. And in the end, the moral order depends on territory, and so it depends on hostility. Its consummate human product: Xenophobic nationalism. Christ, take a look at what's going on in Africa. Christ, we're in the midst of natural man exercising his natural social hate. Aux arbres Citoyens!

BLUNT *(excited, begins to follow Faucets in dance around fire. Takes off shirt from heat. Faucets stooping at more frequent intervals.)* Why don't you embrace women?

ARDENT. Complete anarchists. Men are the social animals. The male of the primate species is the defender of the horde, of its territory, of its fallen. Even dominance, the sheer struggle of it, breeds order. Man breeds social order, women only children. A specialized child-bearer. And take sex, who is really preoccupied with it? Who, the aggressor? What does order mean to women alongside child-bearing and the competitive struggle to latch on to the best-fixed male? You know why so many women are in psychoanalysis? Because we've been fool enough to give women social roles, votes, masculine jobs. They haven't the instincts for it [p. 165]. Can't clean up the mess that's inside.

Anyone takes off shirt and joins procession around fire, which moves into high gear. Only Kung stands aside, wide-eyed. Eve's typewriter beat becomes rhythmical: tap-tap-tap-tap, tap-tap-tap-tap, bell-carriage slide; tap-tap-tap-tap, tap-tap-tap-tap, bell-carriage slide.

BLUNT. The finishing touch, Ardent. Australopithecus. My cave here. My murderous, small predatory carnivore. My ancestor . . . our ancestor.

ARDENT. Yes, yes, the finishing touch, the jewel in man's crown of instincts: murder. All the primates are vegetarians. But what happened to man's line? Came out of the trees, stood up, lost his ripping canines and found his destiny: weapons. Weapons for defense, weapons for meat, weapons for survival. Cain! We are Cain's children, born with weapons in our hands. Oh, not in Asia and not in innocence is man born. In Africa his genesis, and he is nasty, brutish, and short. Man is a predator with a natural instinct to kill with a weapon [p. 316]. No conditioning force has eradicated it, or can. All human history has had one supreme objective: the perfection of the weapon. United Nations, Ha! We are cursed with an irrational, self-destroying, inexorable pursuit of death for death's sake.

FAUCET. But look, Ardent. Zinjanthropus, you know, the one I . . . uh, Mary and I found. No small carnivore predator. Hunted some smaller animals, maybe. Comes after Blunt's old thing. And he probably made those tools, those pebble tools that started the whole Stone Age sequence. How do you fit that in, I mean.

ARDENT (*sneer*). Abel. A freak. A side-branch. Backward, inoffensive, lumbering ape-man. Chewing structure of a vegetarian ape. He lived at the bottom of a well, on treacle, and he was very ill. Obviously then he couldn't have been man's ancestor. Slain by Cain, who took his tools away from him [p. 282]. Simple. And that's it . . . we've got it, the whole of it. (*Stops pacing around fire, whole procession brought up. Ardent is facing fire and audience. Others, save Kung, ranged on either side of him. The typewriter rhythm continues. Ardent shrieks:*) African Nemesis!

ARDENT	CHORUS OF ALL
Man-is-evil	Man-is-evil
Mammalian-boll-weevil	Mammalian-boll-weevil
Was arboreal	Was arboreal
Became predatorial	Became predatorial
And carnivorial	And carnivorial
Also territorial	Also territorial
Status seeker	Status seeker

Property keeper	Property keeper
Instinct lies deeper	Instinct lies deeper
Here to stay	Here to stay
Won't go away	Won't go away
No matter what you say	No matter what you say
No matter what you say	No matter what you say

Ardent climbs on table. Firelight flickers on face. Spreads arms. Typewriter stops.

ARDENT (*frenzied*). Comrades, what to us is this quintessence of evil? Let this be our watchword: Man delights not me—no, nor women neither! To the publisher! (*He rips the sheets out of typewriter. Leaps with a yell toward cave mouth and exit R., grabbing Kung on way. The rest follow running, yelling, save Eve, left alone, sitting at table.*)

EVE (*with compassion*). Oh Ardent, you were a playwright once— but now what lenten entertainment the players shall receive from you. . . . And how do they expect *me* to put out the fire?

Curtain

Act II. Scene 1

The sitting room of a flat in London. Table and chairs R. Door rear center. Members of revolutionary band sitting around. Mary still packs rifle. Ardent in dominant position, sitting on table with feet on a chair.

ARDENT. I'll never understand why the South African government deported us.

KUNG. Maybe the prime minister was jealous.

ARDENT. London's the place for our movement anyhow: the work-shop of Marx, the sanctuary of Freud. Most of all, the very bastille of the romantic fallacy, the British Museum: ivory tower of the world, guardian of the fortress of man's ignorance of man. It's the drilling ground of those snob north-of-the-equator anthropologists who turned their backs on Blunt at the Livingstone conference. . . . (*An idea.*) And we're going to storm it tonight! The manifesto wasn't enough, by God. We need evidence. Evidence, evidence, evidence. That's their anthropological currency and we're going to pay 'em in it. But it won't be easy, because I happen to know they've taken it out of the Museum Library, hidden it from romantic eyes. Look, if people really knew how gibbons lived, how long do you think they'd beat their heads against the stone wall of love, how long could they cherish the hopeless hope that things can somehow turn out for humanity? For an hour today I combed through the Museum Library. Get this: not a single copy of Carpenter's monograph on the gibbon [pp. 36–37]. God knows what else they've sequestered. But I have a good idea where. Old Nose Washtree's office! Third floor of the museum. Come, my guerrilla band. To the Bastille! . . . (*They rise, except Kung.*) You too, Bushman. You're one of . . . us now. And Christ, Mary, leave that blunderbuss here. Those were stone lions in front of the museum, take my word.

MARY. Oh, all right. But may I at least take my pistol?

Curtain

ACT II. SCENE 2

Nose Washtree's office, one hour later. A room lined with books, floor to ceiling. A door to hall R. Large desk with swivel chair L. Curtain opens to empty stage. Door yields under pressure and enter revolutionary band, led by Mary Faucet, waving pistol and motioning for quiet. She turns on light and closes door.

MARY. We're safe now. I'll stand guard. (*Posts self at door.*)

ANYONE. Look at all these books. Wha' does he do with them?

ARDENT (*rapidly crosses to desk, stands in front of it*). All right, everyone. Revolutionary discipline. We have to work fast. Eve, you take that bookcase there (*at R., nearest door*). Faucet, you the next one, then Anyone, then Blunt, and I'll take care of this corner (*largest space. Kung, conspicuously left out, finally gravitates to one of the shelves. Ardent now ranges before books, reading shelf labels.*) European Paleolithic . . . North African Mesolithic . . . A huge compost heap of scientific orthodoxies. I hardly need impress upon you the revolutionary importance of this mission, and now you see its difficulty. The evidence of man's nature must lie hidden as a few slim needles in this great romantic haystack. What are all these shelves? South American *ethnology?* . . . *African ethnology?* . . . *ethnology of the Pacific?*

FAUCET. Ethnology is the study of peoples, the various conditions of mankind, primitive cultures, that sort of thing—hundreds of them, Ardent.

ARDENT. Paleozoic ethnology they never dreamed of. (*Sits at desk with feet on it.*) More things in heaven and earth, oh academics—

EVE. Look, I drew the *sanctum sanctorum* . . . (*puzzled*) so far it is from his desk too. (*Reads titles.*) Das Jean-Jacques Rousseau Problem, The Social Contract (*takes out Social Contract and reads*). The strongest is never strong enough to be always the master, unless he transforms strength into right, and obedience into duty. Hence the right of the strongest, which, though to all seeming meant ironically, is really laid down as a fundamental principle. But are we never to have an explanation of this phrase? Force is a physical power, and I fail to see what moral effect it can have. To yield to force is an act of necessity, not of will—at the most an act of prudence. In what sense can it be a duty?

KUNG (*aside*). They don't make 'em like they used to.

ARDENT. Duty and morals: the royal sceptre and cloak of the most dominant ape, the jabberwocky legitimization of an animal compulsion to rule.

BLUNT (*browsing shelves*). Muckraking. I say, that's what we're doing too, you know. Lincoln Steffens—

ARDENT (*excited*). Yes, yes, look into it, Blunt. Great revolutionary hero, Steffens. Laid bare the natural predatory core of the city. The incomparable urban paleontologist, digging in an Australopithecine underworld of organized crime, organized murder, organized power.

BLUNT (*reads*). I always like to put a story Wundt's assistant,

Külpe, told us after a visit to the neighboring University of Jena to see the aged philosopher Erdmann, whose history of philosophy, in some ten volumes, we had all read and studied. They had a warm, friendly talk, the old scholar and the young scientist, all about the old philosophers and their systems. But when Külpe tried to draw him out on Wundt and the newer school, Erdmann shook his head, declaring that he could not understand the modern men. In my day, he explained, we used to ask the everlasting question: What is man? And you—nowadays you answer it, saying (*voice lowers*), he *was* an ape.

ARDENT. Ach! Nach einmal das Jean-Jacques Rousseau Problem!

FAUCET. Ah, here's a preliminary report from those fellows, Emlen and Schaller, the ones living with mountain gorillas—

ANYONE. No doubt, very happily.

FAUCET. It's buried in this obscure specialist journal, Current Anthropology. (*Takes off glasses and reads.*) It has been possible for Schaller to observe many details of the behavior and social interactions of these animals. He has found a high level of social tolerance prevails among members of a troop—

ANYONE (*quickly interjected*). The primal morality of the in-group, the—

FAUCET. —and even between troops. (*Thoughtfully.*) Several of the troops he has studied include more than one male, and he has never observed signs of aggressiveness among them. Isolated and peripheral males exist, as among other primates; and it is surprising that even these may be accepted into troops without (*voice lowers*) visible displays of antagonism. Neighboring troops have been watched as they peacefully mixed, socialized, and separated. Gorilla troops are apparently nomadic within vaguely defined spatial limits. (*Whispers.*) No traces of territorial behavior have been detected.

ARDENT. Don't let it bother you, old man. Pity the poor gorilla, the harmless Bushman of the higher primates. A dying species, an evolutionary failure. Committed to a forest that has disappeared from under him, he came out of the trees and became a stem eater. His oversized body, his tree-swinger's chest and arms: a mass of architectural incongruities about as meaningful to his present existence as an attic full of memories to a bankrupt nobleman. Doomed by ancient crises beyond control or memory, he knows it, knows it in the balance of instincts which govern his behavior. Vital instincts lose their hold. Primate compulsions fade like color from the skin of the dying. By day he seldom copulates, and by night . . . by night he fouls his own nest! [pp. 112–116]

FAUCET. That's pretty, but is it science?

ARDENT. I detect in you, Faucet, a certain leakiness, a counter-revolutionary romantic tendency, a deviationist drift, a red shift. (*He notices Anyone, who has given up reading and is sitting on the floor.*) What's the matter with *you*?

ANYONE. My lips get tired.

ARDENT. Counter-revolutionary devia— Sh! A noise in the hall! Mary! Mary!

FAUCET (*exasperated*). Not another goddam black-maned lion, not another! Bushman, I told you to stop monkeying around with those paints.

KUNG. But it isn't monkeying.

MARY (*terrified*). Eeek! A mouse (*runs into Faucet's arms. He comforts her. A general hubbub, from which emerges Kung's soothing voice*):

KUNG (*reading*). We walked down the path to the well-house, attracted by the fragrance of the honeysuckle with which it was covered. Someone was drawing water and my teacher placed my hand under the spout. As the cool stream gushed over one hand she spelled into the other the word water, first slowly, then rapidly. I stood still, my whole attention fixed upon the motion of her fingers. Suddenly I felt a misty consciousness as of something forgotten—a thrill of returning thought; and somehow the mystery of language was revealed to me. I knew then that w-a-t-e-r meant that wonderful cool something that was flowing over my hand. The living word awakened my soul, gave it light, hope, joy, set it free! . . . a woman called Keller.

Eve has been absorbed in The Social Contract. She beckons Mary. They sit on the floor, R. Eve speaks sotto voce to her and audience. Ardent engages Blunt in conversation, L., occasionally raising voice enough for all to hear. These outbursts come as counterpoint to Eve's voice.

EVE. This must be *das Problem*. No noble savage here. (*Reads.*) The passage from the state of nature to the civil state produces a very remarkable change in man, by substituting justice for instinct in his conduct, and giving his actions the morality they formerly lacked—

ARDENT. Civilization can never ultimately repress it—

EVE. Then only, when the voice of duty takes the place of physical impulses and the cravings of appetite, does man, who so far had considered only himself, find that he is forced to act on different principles, and to consult his reason before listening to his inclinations—

ARDENT. Conscience as a guiding force in the human drama is one of such small reliability that it assumes very nearly the role of a villain [p. 349]—

EVE. Although, in this state, he deprives himself of some of the advantages which he got from nature—

ARDENT. By nature, a murderer—

EVE. —he gains in return others so great, his faculties are so stimulated and developed, his ideas so extended, his feelings so ennobled, and his whole soul so uplifted, that, did not the abuses of this new condition often degrade him below that which he left—

ARDENT. —the burning flesh of Jews—

EVE. —he would be bound to bless continually the happy moment which took it from him forever, and, instead of a stupid and unimaginative animal, made him an intelligent being and . . . a man. (*She looks at Mary. Mary winks at her.*)

BLUNT (*Sotto voce to Ardent and audience. Interrupted contrapuntally by Eve, still reading to Mary.*) But the Eskimo still baffles me. A complete carnivore he is, and raw meat his dish. The greatest hunter of them all. The bloodthirsty ape in sealskin clothing. Yet look what old Birket-Smith says here. Difficult for the average Eskimo to assert himself against others, he says—

EVE. The social compact substitutes, for such inequalities as nature may have set up between men, an equality that is moral and legitimate. Men, who may be unequal in strength or intelligence, become every one equal by convention and legal right—

BLUNT. And hunting grounds are the property of all and none, res nullius, he says, which not even the tribe can lay claim to. Something else: the Australian Aborigines. Sir Arthur Keith destroyed the Freudian fraud of the primal family by pointing out the Aborigine's larger-than-family society, and we'd go along with that, but you wouldn't want to talk about an Australian band's exclusive territoriality from what I read on these shelves—

EVE. We must clearly distinguish between possession, which is merely the effect of force or the right of the first occupier, from property, which can only be founded on a positive title.

ARDENT (*loudly*). Dammit, these ethnology shelves are useless. What do the Eskimo and all the other timid, shy, cringing, gentle, gauzy, wistful milquetoasts hiding out from mankind on the ice or in the jungle, what do they mean for pristine man? Precisely nothing, and far less that is than the strutting jackdaw. More harmless people, suffering because of their timid dispositions. Who disputes the Eskimo his blubber, his long night, his home built of ice cubes? No one. By adapting himself to a way of life supremely unattractive to Sioux or Apache, a shy creature has insured his survival in perfect confidence that he will escape the notice of all but romantic anthropologists. All that has been actually demonstrated by this (*indicating bookshelves*) loosely disciplined but immensely popular raid into the outposts of man's nature has been that timid people tend to live at unfashionable addresses. [pp. 149–150]

ANYONE. Right again, Ardent. And it goes for Sioux blubber too. They cried when they met people, it says here, in order to manifest the lively joy which they felt in meeting them.

KUNG. Crying can have its own vocabulary.

ARDENT (*sneers*). Now a little child of nature shall lead us.

KUNG. It can happen to people—depends what they call the child. . . . You know, the white shaman comes around and says to me

—me, the magician from way back—I have something new, he says. The latest power, he says, the greatest magic. What, I say. The spell begins like this, he says: in the beginning was the Word. (*Bemused*.) Oh, I tried hard not to laugh, not to his face. Oh, that's great stuff, I said, great stuff. Then he asked me to eat his god . . . and I gave him some of mine. And so I saw the white shaman was far behind the camp of his own people: they had known it all long ago. . . You know, there on the veldt are little white stones on the ground. Now baboons know about these stones, find them lying there. But it's just stones—hard, white, scratchy. To white man they're that too: the same touch, the same color as for the baboon. But then they're something the baboon never will understand—they're diamonds. And not only that—they're wealth: worth getting and giving. And not only that—they're power and they're good, or to some they're power and they're hateful. A whole *world* of name-ideas. More important, more *real* than the touch of it, than the sight of it, than the smell of it. So the white men came to the veldt because of it. And they fought together because of it, and worked together because of it. White men who had been good became bad. Bushmen, who had been bad . . . now they were good: come work for us, nice man, in our holes, they said. The Bushman still smelled as before the stones, as when they drove him out. Now they want us. . . It depends a lot on names.

ARDENT (*exasperated*). Names, names, names. I'm sick of names. The plaintive, inexhaustible primate voice, desperately trying to dupe inexorable vertebrate drives. It's the primeval gene that bursts my spleen, but names will never harm me! (*Flies angrily at shelf, flinging books helter-skelter*.) Oh, just let me get my hands on something we can really use. Some real weapon! I'll forge a knife of prose that will rip those. . . I'll kill the romantic fallacy. I'll murder—(*He finds a small pamphlet. Oakley's, Man the Tool-Maker. Shrieks in triumph. Laughs hysterically*.) Oh, what fools we've been! Taken in by a name —by the same damn device the romantics use to deceive themselves! See this Museum handbook: Man, the *Tool*-Maker. (*Sarcastic laugh*.) *Tool*-Maker. Do you think the British Museum would ever, ever in a million years of orthodox folly,

ever, ever publish a handbook called Man, the *Weapon*-Maker?
[p. 205] Look at these tools. (*Sneer.*) Tools, Ha! Cudgels!
Weapons! (*Dramatically.*) But to suggest that we find in the
competition of weapons the most exhilarating human experience would be blasphemy. Would the Museum dare to provoke in the House of Commons the question period of heroic
proportions? [p. 205] And for a hundred responsible anthropologists gathered in a Rhodesian town to admit—to admit when
Blunt put it to them—that Australopithecus had systematically
used weapons would be to invite a cultural definition of man
as the creature who systematically makes them. Never! Never!
Ha-ha-ha (*waves pamphlet*) but just you wait, Professor Hig-
gins, just you wait. (*Menacingly.*) No matter how eloquently
you say it, no matter what you call it, a weapon by any other
name will kill as neat! (*Leaps to desk, others gather round,
except Kung, who slips out door and runs off.*) Comrades . . .
we have been tried and not found wanting. . . This is our
finest hour. We have tempered the sword of revolution in the
very rose water of the romantic brainwash. (*Exhorts.*) And now
I say to you, surrounded as we are by the pressing weight of
what passes as evidence for those who choose to delude themselves, I say to you. . . Man delights not me—no, nor women
neither!

They exit, chanting, Ardent leading:

CHORUS	ARDENT
Man is evil	Man is evil
Mammalian boll weevil	Mammalian boll weevil
Was arboreal	Was arboreal
Became predatorial	Became predatorial
And carnivorial	And carnivorial
Also territorial	Also territorial
Status seeker	Status seeker
Property keeper	Property keeper
Instinct lies deeper	Instinct lies deeper
Here to stay	Here to stay
Won't go away	Won't go away
No matter what you say	No matter what you say
No matter what you say	No matter what you say

Faucet, lingering, sneaks back, hides a copy of Current Anthropology in his jacket, and hurries out to join the rest.

Curtain

ACT III

An apartment in lower Manhattan, late afternoon. One room flat. Door to hallway at rear. Door to bathroom L. Table and chairs R. Other furniture. Ardent, Anyone, Eve, Blunt and the Faucets draped disconsolately about, Ardent sitting on table, feet on chair.

ARDENT. I should have known better than to take that Bushman into the revolutionary movement.

ANYONE. I still say the Bushman couldn't have known. He ran off before we set up the plan to change the labels on the Paleolithic tools—the cudgels, I mean—in the British Museum.

ARDENT. So my gallant band, here we are. Deported victims of the primate British urge to defend a precious isle of ignorance against the shining sea-terrors of truth.

FAUCET. What time is it?

ARDENT. So little time . . . for it is the time of man, the time out of mind, the time of animal slime beyond all present memory, the time of vertebrate-hate-thy-neighbor, the time—

EVE. It's five o'clock.

FAUCET. Tea-time. No wonder I feel so weary.

ARDENT. What really governs the English—and their out-heroding colonials? Is it a protoplasmic urge to ingest? Oh no. A feudal-primate dominance order? Oh no. Big Ben. Ding-dong! Ding-dong! Ding-dong! Ding-dong! Ding-dong! Drink-tea! Drink-tea! Drink-tea! Drink-tea! Drink-tea!

FAUCET. By God, Ardent, I've had enough! It tolls for thee. To impugn mankind is one thing, but to impugn Britons . . . quite another!

BLUNT. Quite!

MARY. Hear, hear!

ARDENT. The territorial poison quite o'ercrows your spirit.

FAUCET. Ardent, I've long had my doubts—and so have Mary and Blunt, I daresay—about your tactics, but now I question the issue, the whole flimsy revolutionary line. Maybe you've just hit the point. Everyone needs to eat. But we eat at five o'clock, you at six; we tea and crumpets, you ravioli and lemon coke. How does the compulsion account for that? What does govern man, not man in the abstract, but man as he presents himself, man as peoples. Perhaps all men fight and all enjoy pointing the gun, but what governs the historic moment, the episode that is war, and who tells man the direction to point the gun?

BLUNT. In-group amity, out-group enmity, you say, as if it were all so obvious—the modern nation the counterpart of the primate horde. Well it isn't obvious. Do explain to me a nation, Ardent. Act out for me the drama of its beginnings after a million years of tribal history. For the nation is a standing miracle, an evolution, a development of human society that went on record as a denial of the tribe, a denial that the tribal tie is stronger than Americanism, that the stranger was not the fellow. Oh, I'll grant that the nation did not abolish strife, only concentrated it. But if men can live peacefully within the nation after a million years of tribal mistrust, who shall say we have reached the limits of the human conception?

MARY. Once, Ardent, the definition of man was a tribal identity. Navaho means people, Eskimos call themselves the men. But who denies today that he is a member of a planetary race? Man has discovered humanity. And our vaunted ultimate weapon, which shall it strengthen in the long run, the fibers of the nation or the fibers of the world, the idea of a chosen people, or the realization that we're all in this bloody thing together?

ARDENT. A troop of howling monkeys, you three. Poor little monke-ties, lost their crumpe-teas, and they began to cry.

FAUCET. Oh, how tired I am of your secular religion of original sin, without redemption and without morality. What if man's bad? What if he has an urge to possess? Could any human society long survive that didn't define, constrain and satisfy that compulsion on its own terms. What if, as Freud believed, man has a natural propensity to mate with anything in sight? Was ever any human society established on that basis? (*Enter Kung, quietly, unnoticed.*) The urges are repressed, sublimated, twisted this way and that, until in the end man lives in spite of his innermost self. He wars on the playing fields of Eton, dominates by being nicer to others than he is to himself, hunts with paint brush.

KUNG. That's right, you underestimate your player, Ardent.

ARDENT (*and the others*). Bushman! (*Hubbub.*) What are you doing here? (*etc.*)

KUNG. I'm teaching. Primitive religion, at N.Y.U. I just got my Ph.D. at Columbia. In anthropology, of course. Wrote a thesis on the world distribution of theophagy. But I can't say I learned much I didn't know, just a few more names for it. Apparently, you haven't learned much either, Ardent. Bad show, Ardent. The character's still too flat, too stereotyped, the essential villain. And the play, you know nothing about. Like I said, man names things, makes a reality that isn't there, builds it into a system: motherhood, God, fair price, president, twenty dollars or thirty days. And he lives in that reality. It has a name too, I find out . . . culture. I don't believe culture is an inevitable tragedy.

ARDENT. What the hell do those romantics teach in anthropology these days? All the world's a stage? The play's the thing? Well, tell me this: what makes a drama? Do the characters make the play, or the play the characters? Whoever denied that man learns, or that he reasons, or that he can suppress, for a while and in a way, an animal urge? But the frail voice of reason and the timid gesture of the learned response—they are as nothing against the deep command of instinct. And I'll tell you what happens when a basic instinct is held at bay: its energy releases itself through another urge to make its play more terrifying and more irrational. When the Bolsheviks abolished private property, they decreed for themselves a reign of naked power, unleashed a dominance drive that made the English industrial revolution look like a Sunday afternoon picnic on the Thames. The instincts lie deep. They line the human flesh. They are the chemistry of the genes. Cultural instincts, waiting their day. Like a desert river, vanished perhaps season after season, and then, then in a flick of a thunderstorm it comes ripping and raging out of the inscrutable earth. Yes, man builds his own realities. Do you know what it means to believe in the existence of things that don't exist? Self-delusion. All hail, man's unique capacity . . . self-delusion. And against it recollect the ease with which Adolf Hitler brought about in a generation of German youth his education for death. [p. 203] Was this the implanting of a learned response . . . or the release of an instinct? Defend one's own, *Lebensraum,* hate thy— (*Knock at door.*) I'll get it. (*It's Shapiro, carrying a large challah and balancing a plate of gefüllte fish.*) You have the wrong apartment. We didn't order anything. Get out.

SHAPIRO (*politely*). Oh no, you'll excuse me, please, it's the right apartment O.K. Mr. Arbenz? You only today moved in?

ARDENT. Ardent, Ardent—get the name right. Yes, we moved in. We paid our rent. It's our apartment. So beat it!

SHAPIIRO. Vell, you see, ve live down the hall. Shapiro, 2B. And Sarah for the veekend just happened to be making some gefüllte fish. So she says to me, Hymie, why not take some fish to our new neighbors. It's Friday night, maybe they're Catlics? Get acquainted she says, velcome them to the building. Mr. Arbenz, she says, he looks so pale, so bloodless, eat some good . . . Oh, but you'll excuse me. Please, if you're busy, vhy don't you just take the plate and the bread—

EVE (*coming to door*). Please won't you come in, Mr. Shapiro? It's really so nice of you. (*Thank you, thank you, he says, and she and he manage somehow to get the food to the table.*) So thoughtful—

SHAPIRO. Nothing really, absolutely, Mrs. Arbenz. You know, vhen Sarah and I moved in, Mrs. Cassidy, she used to live in this very apartment, she brought us some preserved pig's knuckles that first night. Such good people in this building, so considerate of the others. You know . . . anyhow, taste the gefüllte fish, it's Sarah's best special dish.

EVE (*setting out food*). Here you are, Faucet. Tea-time, old boy C'mon Blunt, Mary, Anyone, Bushman. (*Aside to Ardent.*) Robert, don't sulk. You'll make him feel bad.

Ardent comes to table and starts to cut challah.

SHAPIRO. You'll excuse me, Mr. Arbenz, for taking the liberty. Challah is a kind of bread tastes better it should be torn apart. Here . . . by the nubbles.

BLUNT. How barbarian!

MARY (*sarcastic*). The knife is so much more civilized.

SHAPIRO. Sure, sure, you're right, yes. Then I'll cut it for you. Ve too had problems with the pig's knuckles. Oi! (*cuts finger, sucks blood*) It's nothing, nothing. Eat, eat. Like my mother used to say: eat, Hymie, eat . . . or I'll kill myself. (*Sets plate of fish and bread before Faucet.*)

BLUNT. Faucet, you're pale as a ghost.

FAUCET (*running in screaming anguish to bathroom*). Yeeah! There's blood on the challah!

ANYONE. Did it release his animal instincts?

MARY. His lunch.

SHAPIRO. Vell, you should enjoy yourselves. Sarah said for me I should come right home if they're goyem . . . I mean if they're going to be busy. Come in any time. Shapiro, 2B.

ARDENT (*going to door with him*). Yea, sure, sure . . . and to you the same. I mean, the same to you, you come over here. (*Slams door after Shapiro but then regrets it, so opens it quickly and shuts it again lightly.*)

BLUNT. I wouldn't eat that bloody challah. What's more, I'm fed up with this whole bloody revolution. It's about time, you knew, Ardent. The Faucets and I turned in that fool scheme of changing the museum labels on the Paleolithic tools. It is a science, you know. Just doesn't change like that. Not kosher, you might say.

ARDENT. I was beginning to suspect it. The betrayal, I mean. Incurable romantics. I suspected you all along, all of you. . . Betrayed. Who among us—

BLUNT. Just a second before you produce a new drama, Ardent. Let me tell you just why I'm fed up. It's your mad theory of cultural instincts and compulsions. Vanished like a desert river and then springs up. Shall I gɪˍw a long canine soon, or part the hair of my tail behind? But never mind that. It's just too neat, that's the principal part of it. When we're good to our neighbors, it's the in-group amity of a social species, when we're bad, a primeval urge comes out. When there's no war, the instinct's just in hiding, and when there is war, it springs loose. Let a theory violate my beliefs. Let it even violate credulity. It doesn't matter to me. Nor am I afraid to go against the average opinions of geneticists, physiologists, paleontologists, anthropologists, Rousseau, Marx, Jefferson, or Queen Elizabeth. (Faucet: Come, come.) But I must fear to entertain a hypothesis if I can't imagine a situation in which it would fail to stand up. I must be able to conceive its failure. It's not a hypothesis if it can't be tested.

ARDENT (*shouting*). Of course it's not a hypothesis. You know very well what it is, Blunt. Remember well what I put to you the day you first showed me the evidence of man's ancestral depravity. Dare you tell the world, I asked. Dare you tell a world on the brink of international disaster that man is an innate killer? We have tried everything else, you said, why not try the truth for a change. It's no hypothesis, Blunt. (*Screams.*) It's the truth! The Revolutionary Truth!

MARY (*calm*). No wonder it's proved so immune to evidence. The gorilla—

ANYONE (*sneers*). How does that so-called evidence compare? You know very well what the world is like . . . the Bolshevik terror, racism, the Hungarian Revolution, the burning flesh of Jews, the hundred megatons . . . I know it, and you know it.

MARY. Yes, of course you know it, Anyone. Let's go, gentlemen.

(*She takes Faucet by one arm, Kung by the other. They leave, followed by Blunt, who before he goes, says:*)

BLUNT. Good-bye, Eve. You too, Anyone. Ardent, a horde of gibbons guide thee to thy rest. You can forget the fiver you owe me.

(*Exit*)

ARDENT. Betrayed, betrayed . . . the revolution betrayed. How ungrateful! I was doing it for them. What dogs. What worse-than-dogs. Would a dog betray? Never! (*A thought strikes him*) . . . never. You know, a dog couldn't. Only a man. (*Amazed.*) By God! By God! By God!

EVE. Oh, Robert, Robert, oh hast thou slain the Jabberwock? Come to my arms, my beamish boy! Oh frabjous day. Callooh, Callay!

ARDENT (*musing. He has seen the light.*) Remarkable animal. . . Only he betrays . . . and only he is betrayed. (*Grins sheepishly at Eve. They embrace.*) Ah, Eve. In sickness and in health, in poverty or wealth, a smash or a flop, till death do us part . . . the Eve to my Adam, the Damon to my Pythias, the Horatio to my Hamlet—

EVE. The Sancho to your Quixote.

ARDENT. And Anyone. Dear friend, Anyone. I could always count on you, couldn't I? You'd always believe in me, Anyone. (*Snaps out of it.*) C'mon, it's six o'clock. I'm hungry. I'm taking you both to dinner: a nice, bloody raw steak. On Blunt's fiver. Ha! And then . . . then to a show. West Side Story! (*Puts on Anyone's hat and Eve's coat.*)

ANYONE. Ardent, while you're in the mood, you know I would like to see the United Nations. I've never been in New York before.

ARDENT. No, no, Anyone. Broadway. You'd never understand the East Side Story without the West Side Story. Never.

EVE. Anyhow, the East Side Story'll have a longer run.

ARDENT. Only because it makes war so well. No, the play's the thing. (*Takes both by the arm and shepherds them out the door, saying:*) West Side Story. It's got everything. [pp. 330–33] Natural man. All the instincts right there. The whole damned animal legacy: the timeless struggle over territory, the gangs of primates, the rigid dominance order, the mutual protection of the horde, the collective hate of the others, and then. . . then . . . the unique contribution of man: the supreme dedication to the switch-blade. Absolutely great. West Side Story. Life follows Art!

Curtain

JOHN HURRELL CROOK

The Nature and Function of Territorial Aggression

Ethology and Mass Culture

Within the last few years the young science of ethology has become "popular" with consequences that its more reserved practitioners have yet to comprehend. Television interviews, articles in magazines, comment in the press and books of mass circulation all thrust this rather reticent science increasingly before the public gaze. In addition, when some of its earlier tenets are presented as explanations for human ills in areas seemingly untouched by psychology and social science, it is not surprising that the clamour becomes a marketable product.

Mr. Robert Ardrey, in his introduction to *The Territorial Imperative,* eloquently describes his personal discovery of the huge body of attentive readers his book *African Genesis* had disclosed. Mass literacy provides a market for mass products and indeed a new genre of publication on the problems of animal behavior and their relevance to the "human situation" has come into being; a genre distinguishable in many ways from popular scientific writing of the type presented, for example, by the Pelican books on scientific subjects. In the latter an authority presents a carefully weighted digest of contemporary research and theory for public information and discussion. The new product, burnished and furnished with all the artifice skilled authorship can employ, seeks the simple statement, the dramatic story, and, above all, an essentially sensational account of human troubles that in simple explanation relieves the anxiety born of our massive concern with war, aggression, and sex in a disordered world. A good talking point sells better than serious argument.

It would be dangerous, however, for behaviour scientists to think that such works were merely *kitsch*, mass products for a consumer society, for they are informed by extensive reading of the authoritative texts. Furthermore, the viewpoints presented are plausible, entertaining, and appear to instruct. They also reflect, albeit darkly, the contemporary trend towards biological explanation in both psychology and social anthropology largely the result of two main developments. First, the recent conceptual revisions of motivation theory in ethology have allowed a closer relationship with comparative psychology, so long dominated in America by a theoretical framework derived from behaviourism. Techniques of operant conditioning become tools in motivation research by ethologists, and psychologists pay a new respect to ethological experimentation in field and laboratory. Naturally, unresolved conflicts remain, but enough has been achieved for R. A. Hinde (1966) to subtitle his recent important textbook *Animal Behaviour*, with the phrase *A Synthesis of Ethology and Comparative Psychology*. Second, the study of the relationship between behaviour and ecology and the evolution of animal social organization, for long the field of ethology alone, has attracted the attention of certain social anthropologists (e.g. Fox, 1967) looking for a new derivational approach explaining the origins of human behaviour and social structure in terms of those of our nonhuman forebears.

The question that disturbs the practising ethologist is whether the new genre adequately presents the difficulties inherent in the new orientations of behavioural biology or whether it is a glib or one-sided approach which could bring the whole endeavour into disrepute. As M. V. C. Jeffreys (1962) describes in *Personal Values in the Modern World* it is extremely difficult for the individual subjected to a mass culture to discover the basis for views that affect ethical values—even more so when complex doctrines of social and maybe political relevance are purveyed in popular form and become rapidly the stock subjects for after-dinner conversation and assertion. We shall return to this problem in our last paragraphs. Our first concern is with the adequacy of certain of the popular accounts of ethological theory recently published. Do they really inform as much as they may entertain? Our task is to discuss Mr. Ardrey's account of territorial behaviour in man and animals, a task that leads us also to consider some views expressed in Konrad Lorenz's popular book *On Aggression* (1966), which in certain respects bears the same theme.

Instinct, Territory, and Social Engineering

Anyone who has listened to the film script of *Khartoum* will recognise in Robert Ardrey a dramatist of calibre. In *The Territorial Imperative* the same gifts of authorship are displayed prominently. He has a feel for the beauty of natural environment and the ability to describe the excitement of observing animals at close quarters, be it in the savannahs of Africa or in the plastic dishes of the wormrunner's laboratory, which must be the envy of his less-endowed fellow enthusiasts. He has also read in some depth the detailed studies relevant to his theme. He portrays too with vivid pen the conflicts, joys, disappointments, and the often narrow-minded conformity of practising scientists—a picture of a community of men often far from flattering. For the general reader there is much here to relish and enjoy.

Ardrey is concerned basically with the cause of war and man's unpleasantness to man. His explanation centres upon an account of territorial behaviour. Man, Ardrey tells us, is a species of animal whose natural properties include an instinct of territorial aggression. Territoriality is conceived as an innate character of the human species as a consequence of evolutionary inheritance and, more generally, treated as a genetically determined form of animal behaviour. We find him repeatedly referring to an "instinct" or "force" "called territory" (pp. 59, 62, 166). Territoriality expresses an innate drive to gain and defend property, but, in that animals recognise the rights of ownership and withdraw when threatened by an owner, the behavior reveals individual restraint which is interpreted by Ardrey as a form of natural morality. The functions of ownership are said to be the provision of nest site (in birds), a territorial periphery at which stimulative interaction with companions may occur, and identity in that an individual becomes part of an interacting community. These three points, derived in part from the work of well-known naturalists, are stressed again in the last chapter, although here the order of importance is reversed. The basic primordial psychological necessities to life are now identity, stimulation, and security, all of which the instinctive drive to gain and preserve a territory provides. The fact that many animals do not appear to be territorial is evidently of scant relevance because it is those that show this similarity to man that are the focus of interest.

Ardrey distinguishes between two types of society—the *noyau*—a term lifted from the French text of a work by J.J. Petter (1962) on the lemurs of Madagascar—and the *nation*. The *noyau* is a society of "inward antagonism" held together, Ardrey claims, by the mutual animosity of its members. In species after species, Ardrey reminds us, natural selection appears to have promoted social mechanisms that seem to function for no other reason than to alleviate boredom through the promoting of antagonism and excitement. Why this should be so he leaves unexplained (p. 162), but considers the *noyau* an "evolutionary step towards societies characterised by mutual aid" (p. 167), one, indeed, that provides a primitive security of mutual hate. The other type of society, the biological *nation,* is a social group which must contain at least two adult males and which is separated from other groups by antagonism. In a *nation* joint defence of territory promotes the emergence of ingroup leadership and co-operation. Examples of *noyaux* include herring gull colonies, song sparrow neighbourhoods, the small and solitary groups of *Lepilemur* in Madagascar forests, and the "family" groups of gibbons and *Callicebus* monkeys. Among *nations* may evidently be included baboons, even though territorial behaviour is usually marked by avoidance on the fringes of home ranges rather than aggression, and those diurnal societies of lemurs that live with *Lepilemur* in Madagascar forests. Ardrey leaves the question as to why Petter's six nocturnal species of lemur appear to form *noyaux* while the nine diurnal ones are evidently *nations* unanswered, in spite of the strong ecological clues suggested by Petter himself. Ardrey's distinction between *noyaux* and *nations* is difficult to maintain. His *noyaux* species show very diverse types of social structure from pairs, to colonies, to family parties, to groups;

and the reason why a pair of song sparrows, herring gulls, or gibbons collaborating in rearing young and defending their borders should be distinguished in any fundamental way from groups of baboons doing essentially the same thing is unclear. Certainly the "inner antagonism" of baboon troops is considerable, even though overt aggression is reduced through the social role-playing of animals learnt in relation to their individual dominance, age, and sexual statuses. Ardrey's categories indeed overlap so disastrously that the distinction largely disappears on close examination. This is not to say, of course, that major contrasts in social groups cannot be described by using well-defined natural criteria.

The difficulty is magnified when suddenly we read that Italy is a *noyau,* France (in 1939 without de Gaulle as alpha male) also, but Germany, Britain, Japan, and the U.S.A. evidently not; nor, we may infer, is the Soviet Union. These are the nations. Greece was a *nation* because the Greeks with notable courage threw out Mussolini's soldiers in 1940. Mussolini thought his soldiers belonged to a *nation* but he was wrong. The Jews finally became a *nation* once the hazards of border defence imposed territory upon them, thereby eliciting those instincts they had forgotten for so long.

Ardrey asks how human territorial defence and war arose when man's most immediate ancestors were apparently nonaggressive apes resembling chimpanzees or gorillas. He provides a more or less orthodox interpretation from the authorities, noting the likely effect of increasing aridity in Africa in the relevant time period and the consequent development of carnivorous habits in protohominids. Armed with weapons and searching for limited protein resources supplied by the animals of the plain, men soon began to compete, formed territories, and this foreshadowed the development of the nation-state.

Modern man thus brings with him basic needs for identity, security, and stimulation, all of which are satisfied by territorial behaviour, through which that greatest stimulant, war, has come upon us. Ardrey's philosophy of real estate thus gains biological approval and the only trouble is that, nowadays, the war-game is too hazardous to play. In a chapter called the "Amity-Enmity Complex" Ardrey predicts that the removal of external hazard should result in the increase of enmity within groups. Above all, the removal of war necessitates a substitute, a ritualisation of aggression. The space race, he suggests, is not so much covert aggression but rather ritualised aggression—a game in which our tensions may be resolved without combat. Ardrey then takes from V. C. Wynne-Edwards the concept of "conventional competition," originally coined in a quite different and thoroughly rigorous context, and suggests that through "conventional competitions" identity and stimulation may be provided without the dangers of destructive conflict. The "natural morality" whereby intruders understand that aggression leads to stronger territorial response has not yet been acquired by men, possibly because his carnivorous propensities emerged late. We must learn to know ourselves and devise conventions. Whether morality without territory is for man a possibility remains for Ardrey the final problem.

Although imbedded in numerous digressions Ardrey's argument comes through the noise clearly enough. His book, published in 1967, resembles in certain details the ideas on human aggression published by Konrad Lorenz in *Das Sogenannte Böse* in 1963, translated into English in 1966. Lorenz, the "father" of ethology in its classical period, is justly considered one of the most distinguished of the older comparative ethologists and he has made major contributions to motivation theory, the study of parent-offspring relations and early learning, behavioural evolution, and the use of behavioural characters in taxonomy. He shares with Ardrey a profound concern with the human predicament and, in his book, seeks to utilise ethological concepts, largely of his own original formulation, in explanation of aggression in man and animals. The book, addressed to the general public, resembles Ardrey's in its style of popular presentation and in its selectivity of argument. Like Ardrey, Lorenz adopts a highly personal approach, writes in the first person and, as in his earlier *King Solomon's Ring,* reveals the joy and delight that any contemplative naturalist has in the study of complex animal behaviour. Lorenz considers aggressive behaviour in man and animals to be the expression of an innate drive; an appetite seeking consummation in its expression upon release by an appropriate stimulus presentation. He provides a chapter on motivational studies concerning the "spontaneity" of innate drives, which he uses as evidence for his particular approach.

Aggression is of survival value to its practitioners because it ensures the dispersal of individuals and hence the optimum utilisation of resources. Competition ensures that only the fittest individuals breed. Fighting within groups promotes the formation of hierarchies which allow for the emergence of leadership. Aggressiveness is not, however, directed inappropriately to any member of a species, nor is it biologically advantageous for it to lead to the death of one antagonist and the possible exhaustion of the other. Natural selection has led to the development of postures which signal the submission of one of two opponents thereby reducing the attack drive of the other. Encounters become ritualised into threatening matches—intruders withdraw and owners retain their territories, a tiring opponent signals submission and the fight ceases. Sometimes complex relationships between individuals become based upon such rituals and involve the formation of strong affectional ties. Indeed, strong personal ties appear characteristic of societies within which marked intraspecific aggression occurs. Lorenz thinks that aggressiveness lies at the root of personal affection. Man differs from many other animals in that he lacks major morphological weapons and, in Lorenz's view, has thus never evolved the means of diverting disadvantageous aggressiveness through innate ritual. Man now lives in a society in which there is little acceptable opportunity for the useful or harmless release of his aggressive drive. Furthermore, with the advent of nuclear weapons, man holds the tool for his own extinction in his hands while he is yet unsure of the restraints he can impose on the impulse to attack. Lorenz, like Ardrey, suggests that competitive games provide the outlet for the collective fury of the *nations*. Through ritualisation and sublimation, aggression may be tamed enough to make life tolerable.

Certain assertions occur in both books. First, that man, in common with many other animals, has an innate territorial or aggressive drive seeking consummation in periodic performance. Second, a superficial comparison of animal societies reveals a variety of territorial and social dispersion patterns to which simple survival values are attributed in terms of optimum utilisation of commodities, selective elimination of the least fit, security and stimulation for the survivers. Third, man is defective in his control of his aggression by reason of his recent evolution without concomitant development of innate ritualised restraints. In both books the possibility that the leopard may change his spots through learning is dismissed. The instinct, rather, must be diverted into conventional substitutes for war. The case for social engineering rather than education is complete.

Is the account in these texts a reasonable basis for the inference from animals to man? To find out we must evaluate the key aspects of the story. First, we may pinpoint the main questions.

1. What is the evidence for an innate aggressive drive involving the defence of territory? Is such behaviour really the compulsive, spontaneous, unalterable force it is supposed to be? Or are aggressive animals modifiable, educable?

2. Do biologists really conceive of the survival value of territory in terms of security, stimulation, and identity? Upon what theoretical contributions have these ideas been based?

3. What is the role of territory in man's primate relatives and what may be inferred from this regarding the evolution of his social organization?

4. Is the Lorenz-Ardrey explanation an adequate account of recent ethological thinking in relation to the problems of human relationship?

Motivation and Territoriality

Ardrey repeatedly speaks of a force or instinct called "territory." The meaning of this term requires elucidation. A solitary animal cannot be territorial, for, to show defence of an area, at least one neighbour is needed. The term "territory" cannot, therefore, refer to an intrinsic aspect of the motivation of an individual but, rather, it refers to a relationship between two or more animals with respect to a location. Territory is a "group characteristic" arising out of the cohabitation of individuals in a given locality and which, as a result of their interaction, come to show a particular pattern of dispersion.

Traditionally, ethologists have been concerned with the fixed action patterns common to all individuals of a species population and which are mostly as stable in their manifestation as morphological traits. In many cases there are good reasons for considering such patterns to be more or less directly under genetic influence and their physiological control may be reasonably described as "innate." Lorenz's own work has contributed greatly to the understanding of such movements, the relative stereotyping of which permits their use in the systematics. Similar arguments may perhaps be applied to many of the movements expressive of emotion in primates including man. Species characteristic behaviour attributes such as temperamental traits and other more complicated features cannot, however, always be treated as innate characters. Common conditions of early rearing and parent-child relations throughout a population are now known to account for many regularities. Highly specific modes of learning may account for the elaboration of simple reflex patterns, as in the case of recent studies of bird song. Behaviour observably beneficial to individuals cannot therefore always be attributed, without extensive investigation, directly to the operation of natural selection of genes over many generations. Other processes may be at work. This is a particularly significant viewpoint when "group characteristics" such as "territory" or "dominance" are under consideration. The physical and social environment of a population may impose direct constraints on social structure. A salmonid fish, the ayu, shows territoriality in shallow brooks but moves in shoals in deep pools (Chapman, 1966). Certain rodents may be highly territorial in some environments at certain population concentrations but fail to show such behaviour under different conditions (Anderson, 1961). Populations of vervet monkeys have been found to be territorial in one habitat but to move in groups of contrasting size and behaviour in undefended home ranges in another (Gartlan, 1966). Ecological and social conditions are thus important in determining whether a population does or does not exhibit territorial behaviour. Its inevitability as a species character cannot simply be assumed.

Nevertheless, it is clear that in species which, under given conditions, reveal a population dispersion based on territoriality there must be some behavioural property that induces the members so to distribute themselves. In an important review, Tinbergen (1957) points out that when we are considering the defence of a geographically fixed site or area, territory is the result of two tendencies shown by the owner; first, site attachment and, second, hostility to that class of animals the members of which comprise the rivals or competitors. These two tendencies can occur independently of one another. Thus certain birds make use of regular roosting sites without defending them; and partridges, after pair formation, attempt to prevent the close approach of conspecifics, although this occurs without reference to a particular site. Furthermore, the functions of these two tendencies are commonly different. Tinbergen remarks that Howard's important studies of territorial behaviour (1920) tended to hinder the development of this distinction by focusing attention on their combined effects. "Simply because birds happen to be 'landed proprietors' (Selous, 1933) or, in other words, combine site attachment with hostility, there is a natural disinclination to consider the two aspects separately." Again, in considering territorial maintenance, both attack and escape are involved, and many cases of territorial dispersion result essentially from mutual avoidance rather than from combat. While all these factors combine to produce territorial behaviour, any analysis of its motivational control must consider each facet of the system separately. Several interrelated mechanisms are likely to be at work and susceptible to differential modification under changing conditions of population pressure or environment.

It is clear, however, that the most important element in the complex is the willingness of an individual to fight to maintain ownership when conditions require it to do so. The question is whether an innate drive to aggression of the sort described by Lorenz and assumed by Ardrey accounts for the observed phenomenon.

Lorenz's account of the proximate determination of aggressive behaviour is based upon a formulation of motivation theory largely developed by him in the classical ethology of the 1930's. According to his famous "hydraulic model" of instinctive behavior (see Lorenz, 1950) the performance of fixed action patterns, such as are shown in sexual behavior or feeding, depends upon the accumulation of energy specific to these activities in centres in the conceptual nervous system. Release of this energy occurs when appropriate stimuli are provided, but in the absence of stimulation the energy must sooner or later find an outlet in relation to an inappropriate stimulus or even "in vacuum." Lorenz has commonly used the apparent spontaneity of behavior under minimal stimulation as support for this view. However, the occurrence of aggressive behavior seems rarely to fit such an account even descriptively. Lorenz's ideas were in large measure based upon Wallace Craig's distinction (1918) between the appetitive and consummatory phases of cyclic drives. According to Lorenz's account the action-specific energy appears first as appetitive behaviour and finds outlet in the performance of the consummatory act. In considering aggression Lorenz ignores, however, Craig's (1918, 1928) further and more important distinction between "appetites" and "aversions." Aversive behavior is a response to undesirable or harmful stimulation and persists until the individual flees or until the stimulation is removed. Aggression, which Craig described as an "aversion," occurs in the social context only on the appearance of an offending individual and continues until one or other of the mutual offenders goes away. According to this account, aggressive behaviour is nonrhythmic and lacks an appetitive phase. (See Chapter 5 in Marler and Hamilton, 1966.) There is no theoretical requirement for aggressive behaviour to well up spontaneously without prior stimulation; and this appears to accord well with descriptive data. Studies which have revealed persistence in attacking on reduction in stimulation appear commonly to implicate a learning process whereby the repeated performance of aggression has secured beneficial reward and the response has generalised to a wide range of stimuli. Unusual persistence may also be due to changes in physiological conditions imposed by hunger, for example, or the recent performance of other aggressive acts. There is in fact no uncontroversial evidence that in the absence of stimulation, aggressiveness must find a spontaneous outlet. Lorenz's attempt to justify his explanation of the causes of aggression with descriptions of rhythmic behavior in other contexts is largely irrelevant and fails to convince. In any case, the whole structure of motivation theory in ethology has undergone a major conceptual revision in recent years and even if aggression could be classified descriptively as an "appetite," the simple Lorenz-Ardrey account of its causation would have to be severely modernized. As Hinde (1967) remarked in a critical review: "Since Lorenz claims that his facts are verified and

makes many generalisations with a voice of authority, while ignor-
ing the bulk of the experimental literature on his subject, it is as well
to reflect on them."

In animal societies, individuals do not fight because they have
territories; they have territories because, among other things, they
fight. The territorial context is not the only one in which aggression occurs. Individuals of many species, but by no means all,
maintain a space around their bodies within which they repel approaching individuals. Individual distance infringements both in
wild flocks of certain birds and in caged groups are thus a common cause of aggressive encounters. Marler (1956b) has shown
that at sources of food chaffinch males usually either attack or
withdraw if a companion approaches within about 20 cms. Females
may approach more closely before they are attacked, but if they
are experimentally coloured to look like males then they are repulsed at the same distances as other males. The weaver bird
Quelea quelea, an extremely social species, tolerates approach to
about 4 cms., and in caged groups some individuals rapidly come
to win encounters more frequently than others so that individual
distances are maintained as much by avoidance of attack by relatively subordinate individuals as by actual aggression (Crook,
1961). Repeated encounters give rise to hierarchies, the so-called
"peck order" first described from flocks of chicken. Such dominance hierarchies are also found in many mammals living in social
groups and, as in baboons, may become very complex with individuals playing elaborate roles resulting from their relative dominance, sex, and age statuses. Locations for sleeping, mating, nesting, or for a whole complex of activities can become an external
reference for dominance. The relative dominance of Steller jays at
feeding stations placed in winter at various distances from the
nesting area of the previous season varied inversely with the distance (Brown, 1963). In great tits, robins, and many other species,
interaction occurs primarily at the periphery of a territory within
which intruders invariably flee. External reference for inter-male
dominance may consist in the temporary location of a male's "family," as in wild geese and among male hamadryas and gelada
baboons. Crowding and hormonal states may effect the type of aggressive reference individuals show. In certain fish, birds, and

rodents, high population densities produce a shift from the holding of territories to the maintenance of individual dominance. Chaffinches, which show individual distance maintenance in winter flocks, show an increase in the area of intolerance as the gonads enlarge in spring; this enlargement rapidly acquiring topographical reference and leading to the establishment of territories (Marler, 1956a).

Territoriality is thus a special case of spatial defence not easily separable from the maintenance of personal space. It appears that the intolerance of individuals of certain species to the approach of conspecifics may increase under the influence of reproductive hormones, leading to an increase in individual distance. Much experimental work has shown that testosterone administration lowers the threshold for aggressive response, the hormonal effect being mediated via particular areas of the brain. Other hormones are now known to effect aggression. The ranking positions of starlings and queleas in hierarchies can be altered by the administration of luteinising hormone (L. H.)—experimentals improving their status. In *Quelea* the status ranking of individual birds in small groups may differ according to whether the hierarchy is calculated from encounters due to individual distance infringements on perches or based on the results of competitions for nesting material. Individual distance is maintained by L. H.-mediated aggression while testosterone level affects competitiveness for reproductively valent commodities (Crook and Butterfield, 1968). The relative subordination of female *Quelea* appears due to the inhibitory effects of oestrogen. Aggression is thus not an unitary phenomenon but the expression of the effect of the interaction of a number of factors both intrinsic and extrinsic to the performer. As our structural account of the process becomes more complete, the need to discuss it in terms of "instinct" will disappear (Bolles, 1967).

Increased hunger tends to provoke an increase in fighting through food competition. Many such encounters can be attributed to increased crowding at food sources and a high frequency of infringement of personal space. Some authors have, however, attributed such increases in aggressive encounters to frustration—meaning an interference preventing the completion of an on-going goal response. Certainly there is a great deal of psychological evidence supporting this contention for man (Dollard et al., 1939), but experimental studies with animals have not yet clarified the question. Marler (1957) describes a caged male chaffinch of unstable rank in a hierarchy that developed the habit of making infrequent visits to the food source, remaining there longer than normal and fighting vigorously all others that approached him there. After the completion of the experiment this bird continued to show threat and to attack others at considerable distances whenever it became hungry. Although detailed studies remain to be done, it does not appear difficult to relate, at least in principle, the work on frustration and aggression in man to that on fighting in lower organisms. The complex programming of behaviour through the acquisition of cultural norms in both human and nonhuman primates leads to the inception of much inhibition or delay into ongoing behaviour. Whereas aggression in more primitive animals is elicited by a variety of relatively precise stimuli in given social contexts, the more complex interplay of motives within the elaborate societies of higher animals gives rise to greater problems of explication. At present the use of mentalistic terms such as "frustration" suffice to indicate behavioural contexts in which the threshold of aggressive tendencies is reduced. Continuing research will provide the precise details of the environmental and physiological circumstances attending this fact. Frustration was once considered to be the sole cause of hostility. There is no need now to adopt that view. The alternative, however, is not a nativistic explanation of the type presented in the books under discussion but a closer investigation of the precise conditions under which aggression is elicited in higher mammals.

In higher mammals and in man, as well as in more lowly creatures, the hereditary component of aggression consists in the tendency to react with attack or hostility to certain classes of stimulation. There is, however, as we have seen, no effective evidence for a genetically determined appetite for aggressive behaviour. The social organisation of advanced birds and mammals is, furthermore, known to depend upon the adoption of appropriate roles by young animals subject to learning in "socialisation." Ample work with nonprimate and primate mammals testifies to the importance of various types of learning and other nongenetic factors in the determination of individual temperament and behaviour (e.g. Thomson, 1965; Harlow and Harlow, 1965; and others). It is to be expected, therefore, that the tendency to show aggression may be modified by contrasting socialisation procedures. Freudian analysis has shown that in man, contrasts in toilet training during the "anal period" of maturation produce differing effects with regard to children's compliance or resistance to parental demand. Overpunitive methods tend to produce a fixation of defiant characteristics, including petulancy, pedantry, and overassertiveness involving aggressive elements. Conversely, guidance without punishment yields a more compliant character. The work of Robert Sears and others (e.g. Sears, Maccoby, and Levin, 1957) has shown that aggressive children are likely to come from homes where the expression of aggression is not regulated by family rules but rather is heavily punished. By the age of twelve, however, such children show less aggression than those from permissive homes with neither rules nor punishments. The least aggressive children come from homes which confront them from infancy with strong rules to prevent aggression but in which bad behaviour is controlled in a nonpunitive manner. In such homes praise and affection are balanced against the withdrawal of love when the child behaves badly. It appears that such treatment is effective in eliciting a strong conscience. The child's personality is developed through the necessity to consider his behaviour and decide upon his subsequent attitudes. Much depends upon the nature of parental "permissiveness" and the sort of rules used in family control of aggression. Current research has yet to describe fully these relationships and much work remains to be done.

There is no doubt that Ardrey is right to emphasise the fact that human beings like animals show assertion and aggression of many kinds in relation to the ownership of objects and property and also in relation to ethnic or national territory. Attitudes towards ingroups, out-groups, foreigners, other races, and the newspaper accounts of the doings of other governments and nations must nevertheless be determined in large measure by the cultural concomitants of socialisation experienced in childhood and adolescence. To ignore or dismiss important research on these effects is to abandon the most relevant evidence on the subject.

The Functions of Territory

The problems presented by territorial behaviour in nature remain many and mostly unresolved. Certainly the subject has not received the attention it deserves although current research into both avian and mammalian social organization is rapidly increasing the information available for analysis. The subject has been reviewed several times; the studies by Nice in 1941, Hinde in 1956, Tinbergen in 1957, and Carpenter in 1958 give a comprehensive account of the history of the concept and state of knowledge up until those years. Recent work has tended to see territoriality as part of a wider conception framed, as it were, within the social system of a species itself considered in relation to population dynamics (Wynne-Edwards, 1962; Crook, 1965; Lack, 1966). Ardrey himself provides many good accounts of the earlier investigations and summarises many of the views current until about 1962.

Animals, particularly birds, have been recognised as holding territories at least since the days of Aristotle. Carpenter (1958) describes the history of the concept from Willughby's notes on the nightingale in 1678 to the modern definition of the subject by Altum in 1868, Moffat in 1903, and Elliot Howard in 1907–14 and 1920. The descriptive data showed that territoriality involved the defence of an area more or less well-defined spatially and within which intruders normally fled when challenged, the most aggressive encounters occurring on the periphery of the territory bordering that of another individual. In its territory a bird makes itself conspicuous by vocal or visual display as also do, for example, the males of groups of certain lemurs, the vervet monkey, and the howler monkey, which live in territorial areas. Much of the aggression in territorial defence consists of threatening display or ritualised fighting whereby spacing is achieved with little damage done to the protagonists. Real fighting is, however, not always avoided. In early work the prime functions of territory were considered to be the maintenance of an area ensuring a sufficient food supply for the defender and his family and provision of a topographical focus for mating and nesting. Territory was also considered to be a mechanism limiting the number of pairs of birds in an area by spacing them. Fighting was thought to ensure that the strong rather than the weak reproduced.

The main body of information on territory has come from ornithology. In particular, a great diversity of territorial arrangements has become apparent. In his 1956 paper Hinde classified bird territories into four main types. The first consists of a large breeding area within which nesting, courtship and mating, and most food seeking usually occur; as in certain warblers (*Sylviidae*) and the robin, for example. The second type is a large breeding area but one which does not furnish most of the food, as, for example, in the nightjar, reed warbler, and the Euplectine weaver birds. In the third type, the territory is confined to a small area around the nest as in many bird colonies. Colonial polygamous species may build several nests in a territory. Feeding obviously occurs elsewhere and the spacing effect occurs only within the confines of the colony itself. In the last type the defended area, of small extent, is used solely for pairing or for mating. In gulls, pairing territories exist early in the breeding season separately from those locations used later for nesting. In "arena" birds males occupy small sites often placed closely together and to which females come. The males show elaborate displays and complex procedures exist whereby females choose a mate, the most remarkable system so far described in detail being that of the ruff. In addition, work on the birds of paradise and bower birds in Australasia and the manakins in Central America suggests that the tropical forests hide much that will prove remarkable. After mating, the females of "arena" birds go elsewhere for nesting and rear their young alone. In addition to normal territoriality, birds of certain species defend areas around their mates, their families, their young or a number of young irrespective of parentage, and, as we have seen, themselves. Defence of an area by a group is not common among birds but a number of examples are known. Among the *Crotophaginae* the ani lives in groups of 15 to 25 birds and defends an area around a communal nest in which several females lay (Davis, 1940). The Australian magpie (*Cracticidae*) holds group territories throughout the year and fights in teams, cock with cock and hen with hen (Carrick, 1963). In a number of other species, communalism involving the participation of a number of adults and juveniles in the rearing of young in a territory also occurs.

Among mammals, the family home or nest may be the focus of territorial behaviour, as in many rodents. In other cases, areas may be defended by relatively large groups that may spend some or all of their time there. The vicuna, a species of South American llama, has a system in which a male defends an area against other males and keeps his herd within bounds (Koford, 1957). Red deer move within circumscribed areas (Lowe, 1966), and prides of lions may attack other lions trespassing within their range (Schenkel, 1966). Adult male seals hold territories on beaches where a population hauls out for breeding, and the male Ugandan kob, studied by Buechner, whose report is well described by Ardrey, defends a small territory in an arena. The male kob's behaviour there resembles that of blackcock on a lek. The wildebeest in the Ngoro-ngoro crater near Serengeti apparently are territorial but, on the plains nearby, they defend mobile harem groups during long migrations. As with birds, some mammals are "distance" species and resent close approach, whereas others allow close contact.

In a survey of mammalian territories, Burt (1943) made an important distinction between areas that are actually defended and the area over which a group ranges. In many species, actual territorial defence does not occur and the home ranges of groups overlap markedly. Usually such ranges contain a "core area" in which the group centres most of its activities. Such "home range" systems intergrade with territorial ones, as in cases where groups avoid close contact rather than showing aggression. There is thus a gradient between tightly packed territorial groups and groups wandering in more or less undefended ranges often sharing the use of certain environmental commodities such as good feeding grounds or water holes. An important survey of a variety of such systems has recently been published under the editorship of Peter Jewell and Caroline Loizos (1966).

The very diversity of these mammalian and avian dispersion types suggests that any simple statement about the function of territorialism in general is almost bound to be inadequate. Among the many functions attributed to territory holding have been the promotion of dominance, the selective breeding of the strong, the reduction or regulation of sexual fighting, the enforcement of monogamy, the protection of nests and young from predators, the regulation of group size, the preservation of food supplies, the dispersion of populations, the localisation of waste disposal, and the limitation of the spread of diseases. The condensation of this range of possibilities into abstract principles such as identity, security, and stimulation not only appears premature but neglects the diversity of the phenomena; in different species territories may certainly have functions of widely differing kinds.

Although there is a considerable range both in the referents to which territorial behaviour may be shown and in the types of dispersion produced by it, early work suggested that all forms of territorial aggression, in common with other types of agonistic relationship such as dominance or individual distance behaviour, were due basically to the same motivational source, (Hinde, 1956). Nevertheless, while all forms of fighting are essentially similar, it is clear that the threshold for the elicitation of aggressive behaviour is dependent upon a complex of physiological conditions which may vary independently and change seasonally. This threshold may be expressed as the distance from a territorially valent object towards which approach will elicit attack. Thus some species of bird become aggressive at greater distances from the nest than others. The sensitivity of individuals to the relationship between defended object and the distance at which aggression occurs appears subject to natural selection and—in that characteristic mean sizes of territory have been described for certain species—may be due to factors based on genetic inheritance. If fighting in territorial defence gives reproductive advantages to breeding male birds, for example, it can be predicted that the genetic basis for the trait will become relatively fixed and transmitted from generation to generation.

The fundamental survival values of aggressive behaviour in social life can be conceived only in relation to intraspecific competition. In addition, however, the holding of space appears to reduce direct competition for a commodity and to allow the development of social competition promoting the evolution of ritualised ceremony. Lockie (1956) pointed out that birds which maintain individual distances in winter flocks keep to an interindividual dispersion that reduces actual combat for food. The more dominant animals defeat subordinates in spatial threat during competition for a food object, but the latter, which remain undamaged, can continue to search. Actual combat could damage the subordinate severely and weaken the stronger bird. Nevertheless, fighting for food does occur when starvation is sufficient to override distance maintenance. The effect of a range of individual dominance values in flocks is thus likely to produce differential starvation during food shortage—the more dominant birds being more likely to survive.

Intraspecific competition is most meaningfully discussed in the context of population dynamics. Most bird species in temperate zones show an annual cycle of numbers with marked winter mortality. Following an unusually severe winter, losses are replaced by spring breeding and numbers increase until breeding individuals are forced more closely together in their chosen habitat. There will come a point at which certain commodities essential for life or reproduction, such as nesting sites, appropriate cover, or food, come into short supply. Clearly the type of commodity most likely to fall into shortage will depend greatly on the ecological niche occupied by a species. The successful defence of such commodities will tend to ensure the perpetuation of an individual's genes through successful reproduction and hence the selection of the traits that gave it advantage. Territorial defence is likely to arise in many species but, in that they tend to experience different types of competitive contingency, the sorts of territoriality displayed will be quite diverse over a wide range of cases.

An explanation of a territorial system may not, however, rely only on the concept of the natural selection of genetic factors. While in some species territory size is markedly stable, in others considerable variation is found. Certain swamp-dwelling weavers breed in large territories in small bushes fringing the swamp, but they may also utilise a large tree islanded in the flood wherein they breed in extremely small territories crowded together and forming a colony. The baya weaver of India commonly breeds in large palm trees in colonies, but in homogenous scrubland relatively isolated nests have been recorded. Here the territory size is highly labile, the individual adapting itself to the apparently optimum circumstances in any given locality. Species that otherwise appear to show stable territory sizes are probably affected to some extent in a similar way. For example several British woodland birds breed at greater densities near housing estates, where their winter survival is higher than in natural woodlands, where it is comparatively low. On Mandarte Island, Canada, a population of song sparrows divided up the habitat into similarly sized territories for several years. Then, suddenly, they increased numbers by half as much again indicating that the territory size was not strictly controlling the number of birds present but was rather an expression of it (Tompa, 1964). A similar increase in the numbers of great tits breeding in a wood near Oxford suggests the same could be true for this species. In all these cases then the dispersion of a species population was largely controlled by ecological aspects and population density. Territories, however, appear to be of limited compressibility and hence provide a species with certain environmental qualities without which its members cannot reproduce.

Unfortunately, relatively little experimental work has been done on the territories of wild animals and hence the relative importance of the different determinants of territorial dispersion in any given case remains to be determined adequately. It seems, however, clear that the information required for an adequate account of a given dispersion pattern must come from at least three sources. The first concerns the hereditary traits of the species governing its tendency to maintain the defence of certain commodities and the distances (thresholds of response to intrusion) from these at which aggression will occur. How far such responsiveness is actually inherited or acquired during some process of imprinting in relation to habitat and parental behaviour requires experimental analysis. The second group of factors concerns the relative availability of commodities essential for survival and reproduction. The third set concerns the density of the population and the type of social community in which the population exists. We have already argued that territoriality cannot be conceived as a species property, like leg length or plumage pattern; rather it is a group characteristic expressing the effects of the interaction of individuals with one another and the environment. Territory is but a single aspect of the social system shown by a species. An understanding of the system as a whole is more likely to inform us regarding territory than will the particular study of territory to the neglect of other social behaviours.

In recent survey of avian social systems in relation to ecology,

Crook (1965) examined correlations between some six types of nonbreeding social-dispersion pattern, four types of breeding-season pattern, and a number of ecological characteristics including habitat and food type, food dispersion, and nest sites of 115 avian taxonomic families in which little variation between species in social organisation had been reported. Seventy-nine showed patterns of dispersion involving the holding of sizeable pair territories for breeding. Of these, territory holding characterised nonbreeding dispersion in some forty families. The remaining thirty-nine families showed gregarious flocking outside the breeding season. Twenty-four families showed colonial breeding involving the holding of small territories in densely occupied sites and flocking behaviour in the nonbreeding period. No families, however, showed a pattern involving out of breeding season territoriality with breeding season flocking. The most persistently territorial birds occurred in some twenty-eight primarily insectivorous families, two carnivorous ones, four fish eating, two nectar feeding, and a few more or less omnivorous ones. Almost all these birds must hunt or search for their food and their success depends on cryptic approach, speed, and skill. The relatively solitary nature of these species is therefore considered an adaptation to this mode of food exploitation for which gregarious flocking would tend to be of little assistance. This is, however, not the whole story. When the territorial breeders which flock in "winter" are considered, an association between territory holding and cryptic nest siting in locations not otherwise naturally protected from the approach of predators is found. Protection of nests and their contents thus emerges as an important function of territorial behaviour. The flocking behaviour in the nonbreeding season is related to the utility of rapid congregation made possible at dispersed food sources and to protection against predators. In certain species such as the kingfisher, the linear shape of the habitat along the river banks, for example, appears to correlate with the holding of sizeable territories. The nest site in holes seems sufficiently protective to allow colony formation should this be advantageous. However, an increase in population density in a restricted breeding site would rapidly deplete food resources in the vicinity and necessitate search at a distance. It would be advantageous for members of a species in such a habitat to disperse themselves more "in order" to work less hard in food finding when rearing young. Territory size in such cases may be related to the food content of the territorial area.

Colony formation commonly develops in correlation with evidence that the chosen sites are in some way protective and prevent the intrusion of predators. Dense breeding is also associated with a large surrounding area from which the colony inhabitants may draw sustenance for their young in common. Within colonies the actual spacing of nests may be related to the incidence of predator intrusion. Tinbergen (1953) showed that the herring gull colonies to which predators had gained access had nests more widely dispersed than usual. Among the species of Euplectine weavers those with nests in the most protected places in swamps tend to nest territorially in colonies but those building nests hidden in homogenous grassland have much larger territories dispersed in "neighbourhoods." In this case the discovery of one nest by a predator would not lead easily to the discovery of another.

The maintenance of territories within dense colonies is evidently related not only to the defence of a nest site but more particularly perhaps to the prevention of interference from rival males or females in the pairing and mating procedure of the owners. In weaver colonies, males may sometimes attempt copulations with neighbouring females in the absence of the territory owner, and females may attempt to occupy already occupied nests and have then to be driven out by the owning pair. In weavers, too, a great deal of nest robbing for nest-building materials occurs. In some species with short breeding seasons, males rarely leave their territories except to obtain materials and food in brief sallies. The development of true communal life involving co-operation between members of a group is rare in birds, and limited research suggests it occurs when parents experience difficulty in rearing broods and the participation of juveniles or other "helpers" becomes of selective advantage both to parents and, in their turn, to their helpers. Complex social interactions involving ritualised ceremonies reducing the incidence of intragroup aggression have evolved in some of these groups. Certainly intragroup aggression tends to be markedly reduced in such groups which have sometimes been referred to as "sisterhoods." Some of these groups appear to be "clans"—closely related individuals of two or more generations living together. Such species may breed at considerable population densities and then, as in the well-studied case of the Australian magpie (*Gymnorhina tibicen*), group territoriality appears, the function of which appears related to food supply (Carrick, 1963).

The complex group territories of certain mammals associate both with the defence of females by a male and with the holding of a relatively well-defined area (i.e. the vicuna) within which the food supply is located. In the "arena" breeders such as the kob, territory holding is related to competition between males for the sexual attention of females, and the holding of space prevents or greatly reduces the likelihood of interference with mating once it starts. Among seals and sea lions, males hold territories that contain their "harems."

While the diversity of cases is considerable and each requires detailed individual analysis, enough has been said to suggest that among the main functions of territory holding are: the maintenance of dispersion, so that individual hunting techniques may be performed without interference; the maintenance of an area providing a food supply requisite for rearing young or maintaining group existence; the reduction of crowding of cryptic nests so as to reduce the likelihood of their discovery by predators; and the prevention of interference with nesting, courtship, mating, and sometimes the rearing of young. We need not quibble with Ardrey over his use of the blanket term "security" to cover all these cases. We should, however, stress that the diversity of functions that territory holding performs is a consequence of adaptive radiation of species into a wide variety of ecological niches. The nature of competition imposed by the adaptations of a species to a given habitat defines the type of territorial behaviour seen.

Ardrey is right to point out that many territories occur in neighbourhoods or colonies and that equally suitable areas may remain unoccupied. He discusses this in terms of the stimulation evoked by the defence of territorial peripheries but he does not treat its probable function. Darling's (1938) original suggestion referred to the possibility that the social stimulation of colonial life helped to synchronise breeding, thereby reducing the length of the breeding period which in turn decreased the period of heavy predation on young. His data did not, however, prove the point unequivocally, and it remains a fascinating hypothesis. The role of behavioural interaction in promoting breeding synchronisation has, however, been accepted by several recent authors with particular reference to colonial birds. Synchronisation may function in at least two ways. First, it may ensure that as many birds as possible start breeding early in a short breeding season and this increases the likelihood of their rearing young in the annual period of optimum food supply. Second, the mass departure of young may reduce the effects of predation. In theory at least, if the young birds were leaving at staggered intervals a greater number would fall foul of the waiting carnivores. Should these hypotheses be tested in further studies such as those by Patterson (1965) and generally confirmed, the survival value of social stimulation will be seen as a consequence of environmental adaptation rather than as providing excitement of value in itself, as Ardrey seems to suggest.

One of the effects of holding a sizeable area of land for breeding is certainly to space out the individuals of a population. V. C. Wynne-Edwards (1962) has suggested that not only is the prime function of territory to produce dispersal but that dispersion itself functions to control population size (see also Moffat, 1903). This hypothesis forms part of a broader theory which holds that social organisation is essentially a mechanism for providing "conventional competition" whereby numbers are regulated by homeostatic dispersal in relation to food resources. Populations are thereby believed to maintain optimum numbers in relation to resources. Competition is said to be conventional in that its putative function is to measure the density of the population present and relate the finding to food supplies. If the indicated numbers are likely to over-exploit the actual supply an exodus of the surplus population follows. Territorial competition is treated as a convention having these supposed advantageous effects. It is true that dispersal may result from territorial behaviour but the suggestion that this is a primary survival value is far from proven. Territorial behaviour could have this effect even if the functions for which it was evolved were quite different. In any case our comparative study of the range of territory types shows that only some of them could function in the way Wynne-Edwards's theory requires and none of them need necessarily do so.

Wynne-Edwards's hypothesis regarding the significance of social structure has received much criticism and appears unlikely to prove acceptable in its entirety (Crook, 1965; Lack, 1966; and others). The evidence from field studies relating population dispersion to the natural control of numbers and territorial behaviour is furthermore highly inconclusive. Lack (1966) has recently surveyed the findings of several of the more detailed ornithological reports on the relation between territoriality and population control. For example, each pair of wood pigeons defends an area around its nest and the resultant spacing probably assists the concealment of nests from predators. The birds, however, feed in flocks; the territory cannot therefore conserve a food supply and there is no reason to think it regulates numbers. In other species, population is known to be regulated by actual food shortage rather than by any factors producing dispersion. Again, as we have already remarked, both the song sparrow on Mandarte Island and great tits at Oxford showed numbers of breeding birds that in certain years greatly exceeded the usual population of the study area so that the average territory size seems to have little to do with the control of numbers. In some species, however, such as the red grouse and ptarmigan in Scotland and the population of skylarks studied at Ravenglas, breeding density is related to the holding of territories, and unsuccessful birds are pushed into peripheral habitats and fail to reproduce (e.g. Jenkins, Watson, and Miller, 1963; Watson, 1965; Delius, 1965). Older work on great tits in Holland had also indicated that in a particular habitat territorial behaviour set an upper limit to numbers (Kluijver and Tinbergen, 1953).

It seems, in fact, certain that in contrasting habitat conditions different factors will play the crucial role of key constraints imposing density-dependent mortality (see Cody, 1966; Blank, Southwood, and Cross, 1967; Southwood, 1967). In environments subject to severe winter mortality involving food shortage, the numbers of birds present may rarely reach such proportions that territorial behaviour limits their settlement for breeding. In richly endowed habitats, however, or in particularly stable ones, territorial behaviour may become the prime constraint controlling breeding density. The relative frequency of such cases remains to be determined. Their effective demonstration, however, would not necessarily establish Wynne-Edwards's contention. Territorial competition may be "real" rather than "conventional" in that without the maintenance of space for uninterrupted mating, for example, breeding might not be able to occur at all. Exclusion of some individuals from breeding would then be an effect of competitive social behaviour of a functional value to the successful individuals of the species for reasons unconnected with dispersal. The overall social system is best conceived as an open arrangement controlled by inputs from factors both intrinsic and extrinsic to the structure itself rather than a biotic adaptation especially evolved for population control.

Finally, we should again emphasise that social systems are characteristics of groups. Discussion of their "evolution" poses a number of semantic problems akin to those involved in the treatment of the evolution of ecological communities (Williams, 1966). Social systems develop historically through interactive effects of population size, social behaviour, and environment. Their control is not a "property" of the species in question but rather lies in the relations its members have established with one another and with the features of their habitat. Evolution by the natural selection of the genetic endowment of the population forms only a part of this historical process. If these arguments are found to be sound then Wynne-Edwards's technical use of the term "convention" is of doubtful explanatory value. Its adoption by Ardrey without an adequate examination of Wynne-Edwards's theory adds nothing to current usage. Football matches and the space race may well be "conventions" but the link between them and biological theory is not established.

Primates, Man, and Territory

Perhaps the most striking feature of those nonhuman primates the behaviour of which is of most relevance to man is precisely their lack of easily defined territorial behaviour. There have been several recent surveys of this material (e.g. Hall, 1965; Washburn, Jay and, Lancaster, 1965; Crook and Gartlan, 1966; Rowell, 1967) and space allows only brief discussion here. Comparative studies of forest fringe, and savannah *Cercopithecus* and *Macaca* monkeys, the baboons of the genera *Papio* and *Theropithecus,* the chimpanzee and gorilla do not provide evidence of rigorously defended territories. On the other hand, populations of several forest primates in Madagascar, Africa, and South America do defend group territories by means of elaborate vocal and visual displays, border skirmishing and olfactory marking in some cases. These species are, however, of less relevance to man than the savannah monkeys and the great apes.

Several kinds of social organisation in the African grasslands and savannah have been reported. All are complex and consist either of troops containing several males and rather more females with attendant juveniles, or of single males with "harems" of females, again with their young. In the latter case groups of nonreproductive and usually subadult males move separately from the reproductive units. The multimale troop is well known from the research of K. R. L. Hall, S. L. Washburn, I. DeVore, and Thelma Rowell on *Papio ursinus, P. cynocephalus,* and *P. anubis* and from Altmann's and Southwick's studies on the rhesus monkey on Cayo Santiago Island and in India. In addition, detailed studies have been made on the Japanese macaque. The one-male reproductive unit has been reported from *Papio hamadryas,* the patas monkey, and the gelada baboon. In the former the units tend to comprise subunits of large troops which may coalesce to form herds. In the patas they move separately in large home ranges, whereas in the gelada they congregate in large herds over good grazing but tend to scatter and forage separately in the dry season of poor food availability. In *Papio ursinus,* the macaques, and the patas the social units forage within large home ranges which tend to overlap to varying extents. Dispersion is maintained mostly by the withdrawal of the intruders. "Ritualised" border encounters do not occur but, in certain unusually structured environments such as temple precincts in India, rhesus troops coming suddenly upon one another may fight, in which case individuals will inflict severe injury upon one another. In the gelada even the maintenance of home ranges is uncertain. Certainly gelada herds comprise any number of reproductive units and all-male groups each of which is quite free to enter or leave a congregation and to travel separately over several miles. While populations utilise core areas in particularly appropriate parts of their habitat, there seems no behavioural factor preventing their wandering off and joining any other feeding congregation at considerable distances from their usual foraging area. No evidence of avoidance of any kind has been seen.

Gorillas forage within large home ranges that overlap extensively and there is no clear evidence of marked avoidance, although a preference for small group life is evident. Chimpanzees live in "open groups" with considerable interchange of membership and all appear to utilise a common range of sizeable extent (Reynolds, 1965).

All these social groupings are extensively structured owing to complex relations between individuals dependent upon relative dominance, age, sex, the adoption of particular roles, and the formation of friendships. Compared with most nonprimate societies, life for these animals is a particularly rich social experience.

The adaptive significance of these different types of society has received some recent attention, and they can be related quite clearly to different environmental contingencies—the nature and availability of sleeping sites, the abundance and seasonal dispersion of food supplies—and to predation pressures. Precise details, however, remain to be worked out. The process whereby this adaptation of society to environment occurs is clearly complex and appears to depend upon the establishment and maintenance of learnt traditions of a protocultural kind gradually acquired by the phenotypic adaptations of individuals to their home locality and social group repetitively over many generations. Social structure is furthermore apt to differ in subtle or pronounced ways in different localities, thereby emphasising the importance of the direct effect of contrasts in environment. Although innate behaviour patterns play important roles in communication of affect within these groups there appears to be no case for suggesting that "instinct" plays a major role in the moulding of social structure as such. This is probably also the case in other advanced nonprimate mammalian societies, few of which have yet been studied in any detail.

Both Rowell (1966) and Crook (1967) have pointed out that where social structures of a primate species appear relatively specific the ethologist, traditionally a student of innate behaviour patterns, could be misled into making incorrect assumptions concerning the origins of the systems observed. Rowell's detailed studies in field and laboratory have amply demonstrated the importance of social learning in the structuring of groups. Learning is a continuous process and the individual's behaviour is markedly adaptable in relation to changes in natural reinforcement contingencies. Hall (1963) has stressed the importance of observational learning in monkey groups; the experience of one animal is witnessed by others and the information obtained utilised by them on later occasions. Social structures appear to diverge in contrasting or changing ecological conditions owing to shifts in reinforcement contingencies controlled by such factors as the frequency of food finding, hours needed for satiation, spacing of individuals in relation to food dispersion, size of food object, frequency of food antagonism, and time available for playful interaction and social grooming. Life for these animals may be conceived in terms of sets of complex natural learning "schedules," each providing various types of reward. In particular, the time needed for foraging, the patterns of spacing best suited for search, and the rate of movement required for optimum reward will effectively ration the time available in the day for social activities. Crook and Aldrich-Blake (1968) recently related the rather stereotyped behaviour of geladas at a site in Ethiopia to the long hours they had to spend feeding. Doguera baboons in woods nearby obtained food in larger units and spent less time foraging and more time in social interaction. Their more flexible, reflective behaviour in relation to the presence of the observers might be meaningfully related to these contrasts.

It has been argued that the one-male groups of geladas and certain other primates are sociological adaptations to arid environments (e.g. Crook and Gartlan, 1966). One large male is adequate for the fertilisation of several females and exploits a low percentage of the food available to the nomadic group. The reproductively more important sex then tends to get the most food. Large troops with many adult males are typical of richer environments with both more food and more predators. In arid country individual males and females appear to contribute more to the next generation by living in one-male groups than they would in larger social units that would tend to overexploit the resources of the ground over which they ranged. Probably increasingly arid environments impose splits in troops so that small parties wander separately. Indeed, there is evidence from Japanese macaques and African baboons to support this view. Competition between reproductive males for females in small parties would then tend to produce the separation of subordinate and juvenile males into their own parties, leaving single males in reproductive units. The adaptation to environment in this case thus appears essentially phenotypic. Such changes would appear, however, to initiate new patterns of social and sexual selection such that individuals of differing temperament from those in the parent society may gain reproductive advantages. Concomitant shifts in the genetic basis of individual behaviour may occur and have the effect of stabilising the patterns of interindividual interaction and hence the social structure as a whole.

As Ardrey says, the reappearance of aggressive territory holding in man contrasts strongly with the relatively peaceable affairs of other higher primates. The advent of carnivorous habits, use of weapons, and competition between groups for limited sources of animal protection are indeed the most likely original causes. It seems that the emergence of the new territoriality involved shifts in social traditions in relation to ranging and an acquired lowering of the threshold for aggression towards out-groups as a result of repetitive experiences of hunger and ultimately an intellectual appreciation of its cause. Certainly our modern appreciation of the important role of learning and tradition in the maintenance of non-human primate societies would lead us to emphasise this kind of historical change rather than the possible development of a territorial instinct of the type Ardrey requires.

This is not to deny, however, the probability that changes in human social organisation and the adoption by man of carnivorous feeding habits may not have affected his aggressive reactivity through the selection of certain inherited traits rather than others. Certainly the necessity for increased control of individual behaviour in relation to hunting and role playing in co-operative social life will have entailed the marked development of the ability to delay responding, to interiorise and reflect on alternative causes of action, and to cope with motivational frustration. Aggression itself would have become increasingly complex in manifestation and often separated in time from the events that lowered the threshold for its expression. The hunter's pleasure in killing prey may also have arisen at this time and the "cruelty" inflicted on the "game" animals thus became available for translocation into a social agonistic context.

The development of ownership of tools, homesteads, and domestic animals would greatly have increased the opportunities for conflict within communities, these things becoming in effect extensions of a person's "individual distance." Complex patterns of conventional behaviour (in the usual sense of the word) would arise, giving way in due course to codified laws concerning property and its exchange. International conduct may be conceived as an extension of this principle to a community and political level.

Early in his book Ardrey remarks that "there will remain always the chance that what we observe in man is a kind of mirror held up to nature; our culture and our learning reflect the natural way without in a biological sense being beholden to it" (p. 103). The likelihood that the motivational control of territorial behaviour in man is at a different level from that of fishes and birds suggests that human resemblances to the lower animals might be largely through analogy rather than homology. Indeed this is certainly the impression given by a careful reading of the several papers comparing man and animals at the 1963 symposium on "The Natural History of Aggression," in London (Carthy and Ebling, 1964). Ardrey fails to recognise that the great advances in learning ability and intelligence in the higher mammals mean that historical change through "cultural" processes is possible among them too and the concept need not be reserved for man alone. Man is indeed an animal—but we should not forget his primate status and the behavioural complexity of his relatives. The idea that "the territorial nature of man is genetic and ineradicable" would appear unnecessarily parsimonious.

Conclusions

By adopting a limited Lorenzian view of the nature of aggression Ardrey ignores most of the experimental ethological literature on the subject. Instead of resulting from an innate and ineradicable force demanding repetitive expression, aggressive behaviour occurs normally as a response to particular aversive stimuli and ceases upon their removal. The prevalence of aggression in modern man may thus be attributed to aversive features in the complex overcrowded, overcompetitive, overstratified social world in which he lives rather than to some unsatisfied vital urge. In man, also, aggression is commonly associated with frustrations born of the delay in responding imposed largely by his learning to play social roles in a community. There is every reason to suppose that individual sensitivity to stimuli likely to evoke aggression is determined during socialisation. The manifestation of aggression in human society is thus largely a cultural attribute.

Ardrey's account of the function of territoriality in terms of identity, security, and stimulation is derived from ethological research reports concerned largely with the adaptive significance of behaviour. He provides little detailed discussion on the evolutionary significance of social behaviour in relation to the adaptations of members of a population to their physical and social environment. In this paper this problem is treated at length to clarify the arguments presented in the sources. In discussing man Ardrey gives his three terms a motivational significance in which they represent needs satisfied by the holding of territory. Reflection brings to mind, however, many individuals, who in their maturity found identity, security, and excitement in activities far removed from real estate of any kind. If an instinct is present in a species it should be apparent in the individual members.

Man's nearest relatives among primates are singularly lacking in simple territorial behaviour. Man's recovery of this attribute may be seen as a continuation of trends already present in protocultural social organisations found in primates and originally influenced by acquired carnivorous feeding and competition for sources of protein. There is no need to explain the behaviour in excessively parsimonious terms based on a misleading and outdated account of aggressive behaviour in lower organisms. The relevant hypotheses lie nearer home.

The behaviour of crowds watching "conventionally" competitive sports often indicates the arousal of aggressive attitudes rather than their happy sublimation. Further, the behaviour of players cannot always be recommended. The wanton destruction of train interiors by British football team supporters on the way to an "away" fixture

certainly reveals a release of social tensions in what would appear
to be highly convivial surroundings. Indeed, the holding of major
sporting events is often manageable only when effective rules of
crowd control are operative. As an example of social engineering
such conventions alone seem to achieve little in enhancing human
conduct. Man's aggressive potential is hardly likely to be controlled
solely by attempts at redirection or sublimation. The solution must
lie rather in detailed research into those aspects of human experience which influence aggressive reactivity. In particular the problem concerns those patterns of socialisation and education that give
rise to hostile feelings towards the stranger and the out-group. The
development of attitudes remains an area as yet poorly explored by
psychologists, but with an increasing grasp of experimental techniques there seems no reason to abandon hope for the future. Social psychologists are well aware of these problems and strive to
find solutions. That their efforts so far may appear academic and
slightly naïve is related to the novelty of the research, the complexity of the subject matter, and the youth of this branch of science. The biological basis of human life and its evolutionary history are of great relevance to this enquiry but only when a proper
understanding of the advanced level of social organisation and its
control in higher primates is taken into account. The promulgation
of one-sided and misleadingly simplified doctrine is of no assistance
to those concerned and could lead them to neglect those highly relevant contributions that modern ethological theory and experimental method can legitimately supply.

The merit of *The Territorial Imperative* is to have brought an
awareness of a major research problem to the attention of many
who may not have considered it seriously before. The book nevertheless leaves an unfortunate impression. Apart from its faulty
statement of current ethological theory, the view of life—the
Weltanschauung—portrayed is unhappily pessimistic and for a
wrongly conceived reason. Sir Julian Huxley, in a treatment of the
relevance of biology to man, once argued strongly against "nothing
but-ism" as an unhealthy attitude of unreflective science. Was man
indeed "nothing but" a creature of overpowering destructive impulse, hope for the future would be dark. These decades present
the advanced technological nations with problems of menacing

proportions. Men everywhere are potential victims of an unparalleled background anxiety magnified and reflected at every turn by mass media of communication. The image of man, already demoted from his place near the angels through the popularisation of Darwinian and Freudian ideas, is all too vulnerable to further erosion. The *Zeitgeist* extols the mechanism, and we may perhaps see ourselves as no more than that; but the mechanism is wonderfully complex, its properties poorly understood, and as subjects we remain uniquely self-aware. Although the phenomenon of man cannot be explained by simplistic argument pandering only to the pessimism of an age, the image that most of the people acquire is apt to shape the values of a community. Indeed, a parallel is apparent in the recent past when ideas derived from a misunderstanding of "Social Darwinism" played their part in the history of European fascist politics. Who knows whence a "New Right" may gather a cloak of respectability to condone, perhaps in some new "Report from Iron Mountain," the defence of racial garrisons in the *noyaux* of the near future? The new genre of popular biological exposition neglects the humanity of man. We would do well to meditate upon the reasons.

REFERENCES

Anderson, P. K. (1961). Density, social structure and non-social environment in house-mouse populations and the implications for regulation of numbers. Trans. N.Y. Acad. Sci. Ser. II, 23, (5): 447–451.

Ardrey, R. (1967). The territorial imperative. A personal inquiry into the animal origins of property and nations. London.

Blank, T. H., T. R. E. Southwood, and D. G. Cross. (1967). The ecology of the partridge. 1. Outline of population processes with particular reference to chick mortality and nest density. J. Anim. Ecol. 36: 549–556.

Bolles, R. C. (1967). Theory of motivation. New York.

Brown, J. C. (1963). Aggressiveness, dominance and social organisation in the Steller jay. Condor 65: 460–484.

Burt, W. H. (1943). Territoriality and home range concepts as applied to mammals. J. Mammal. 24: 346–352.

Carpenter, C. R. 1958. Territoriality. *In* Behaviour and evolution. A. Roe and G. G. Simpson (eds.). New Haven.

Carrick, R. (1963). Ecological significance of territory in the Australian magpie, *Gymnorhyna tibicen*. Proc. 13th Int. Orn. Congr. 740–753.

Carthy, J. D. and F. J. Ebling (eds.). (1964). The natural history of aggression. London.

Chapman, D. W. (1966). Food and space as regulations of salmonid populations in streams. Amer. Nat. 100: 345–356.

Cody, M. J. (1966). A general theory of clutch size. Evolution 20: 174–184.

Craig, W. (1918). Appetites and aversions as constituents of instincts. Biol. Bull. 34: 91–107.

Craig, W. (1928). Why do animals fight? Int. J. Ethics. 31: 246–278.

Crook, J. H. (1961). The basis of flock organisation in birds. In Current problems in animal behaviour. W. H. Thorpe and O. L. Zangwill (eds.). Cambridge.

Crook, J. H. (1965). The adaptive significance of avian social organisations. Symp. zool. Soc. Lond. 14: 181–218.

Crook, J. H. (1967). Evolutionary change in primate societies. Sci. J. 3. 6: 66–72.

Crook, J. H. and P. Aldrich-Blake. (1968). Ecological and behavioural contrasts between sympatric ground-dwelling primates in Ethiopia. Folia Primat. In press.

Crook, J. H. and P. A. Butterfield. (1968). Effects of testosterone propionate and luteinising hormone on agonistic and nest building behaviour of captive *Quelea quelea*. Anim. Behav. In press.

Crook, J. H. and J. S. Gartlan. (1966). Evolution of primate societies. Nature. Lond. 210: 1200–1203.

Darling, F. F. (1938). Bird flocks and the breeding cycle. A contribution to the study of avian sociality. Cambridge.

Davis, D. E. (1940). Social nesting habits of the smooth-billed ani. Auk. 57: 179–218.

Delius, J. D. (1965). A population study of skylarks, *Alauda arvensis*. Ibis 107: 465–492.

Dollard, J. et al. (1939). Frustration and aggression. New Haven.

Fox, R. (1967). In the beginning: aspects of hominid behavioural evolution. Man. 2: 415–433.

Gartlan, J. S. (1966). Ecology and behaviour of the vervet monkey. Lolui Island. Lake Victoria. Uganda. Ph.D. Thesis. Bristol Univ. Library.

Hall, K. R. L. (1963). Observational learning in monkeys and apes. Brit. J. Psychol. 54: 201–226.

Hall, K. R. L. (1965). Social organisation of the old world monkeys and apes. Symp. zool. Soc. Lond. 14: 265–290.

Harlow, H. F. and M. K. Harlow. (1965). The affectional systems. *In* Behaviour of non-human primates. Vol. 2. A. M. Schrier, H. F. Harlow, F. Stollnitz (eds.). New York.

Hinde, R. A. (1956). The biological significance of the territories of birds. Ibis 98: 340–369.

Hinde, R. A. (1966). Animal behaviour. A synthesis of ethology and comparative psychology. New York.

Hinde, R. A. (1967). The nature of aggression. New Society. 2nd March.

Howard, H. E. (1907–14). The British warblers, a history, with problems of their lives. 6 vols. Cambridge.

Howard, H. E. (1920). Territory in bird life. London.

Jeffreys, M. V. C. (1962). Personal values in the modern world. London.

Jenkens, D., A. Watson, and G. R. Miller. (1963). Population studies on red grouse, *Lagopus lagopus scoticus*. J. Anim. Ecol. 32: 317–376.

Jewell, P. A. and C. Loizos (eds.). (1966). Play, exploration and territory in mammals. Symp. zool. Soc. Lond. 18.

Kluijver, H. N. and L. Tinbergen. (1953). Territory and the regulation of density in titmice. Arch. Nethl. Zool. 10: 266–287.

Koford, C. B. (1957). The vicuña and the puna. Ecological Monographs 27: 153–219.

Lack, D. (1966). Population studies of birds. Oxford.

Lockie, J. D. (1956). Winter fighting in feeding flocks of rooks, jackdaws and carrion crows. Bird Study 3: 180–190.

Lorenz, K. (1950). The comparative method in studying innate behaviour patterns. Symp. Soc. Exp. Biol. 4: 221–268.

Lorenz, K. (1963). Das Sogenannte Böse. Vienna.

Lowe, U. P. W. (1966). Observations on the dispersal of red deer on rhum. Symp. zool. Soc. Lond. 18: 211–228.

Marler, P. R. (1956a). Territory and individual distance in the chaffinch (*Fringilla coelebs*) Ibis 98: 496–501.

Marler, P. R. (1956b). Studies of fighting in chaffinches. (3) Proximity as a cause of aggression. Brit. J. Anim. Behav. 4: 23–30.

Marler, P. R. (1957). Studies of fighting in chaffinches (4). Appetitive and consummatory behavior. Brit. J. Anim. Behav. 5: 29–37.

Marler, P. R. and W. J. Hamilton. (1966). Mechanisms of animal behavior. New York.

Moffat, C. B. (1903). The spring rivalry of birds, some views on the limits to multiplication. Irish Nat. 12: 152–66.

Nice, M. M. (1941). The role of territory in bird-life. Amer. Midl. Nat. 26: 441–487.

Patterson, I. J. (1965). Timing and spacing of broods in the black headed gull. *Larus ridibundus.* Ibis 107: 433–459.

Petter, J. J. (1962). Recherches sur l'écologie et l'éthologie des Lemuriens malgaches. Mém. du Mus. Nat. de l'Hist. Naturelle. Sér. A, 27. Fasc. 1. Paris.

Reynolds, V. (1965). Some behavioural comparisons between the chimpanzee and the mountain gorilla in the wild. Amer. Anthropologist. 67: 691–706.

Rowell, T. E. (1966). Forest living baboons in Uganda. J. Zool., Lond. 149: 344–364.

Rowell, T. E. (1967). Variability in the social organisation of primates. *In* Primate ethology. D. Morris (ed.). London.

Schenkel, R. (1966). Play, exploration and territoriality in the wild lion. Symp. zool. Soc. Lond. 18: 11–22.

Sears, R. R., E. E. Maccoby, and H. Levin. (1957). Patterns of child rearing. New York.

Selous, E. (1933). Evolution of habit in birds. London.

Southwood, T. R. E. (1967). The interpretation of population change. J. Anim. Ecol. 36: 519–530.

Thomson, W. R. (1965). The behaviour of offspring. Sci. J. August: 45–50.

Tinbergen, N. (1953). The herring gull's world. Collins. London.

Tinbergen, N. (1957). The functions of territory. Bird Study 4: 14–27.

Tompa, F. S. (1964). Factors determining the numbers of song sparrows *Melospiza melodia* (Wilson) on Mandarte Island. B. C. Canada. Acta. zool. Fenn. 109: 1–68.

Washburn, S. L., P. C. Jay, and J. B. Lancaster. (1965). Field studies of old world monkeys and apes. Science 150: 1541–1547.

Watson, A. (1965). A population study of ptarmigan (*Lagopus mutus*) in Scotland. J. Anim. Ecol. 34: 135–172.

Williams, G. C. (1966). Adaptation and natural selection. A critique of some current evolutionary thought. Princeton.

Wynne-Edwards, V. C. (1962). Animal dispersion in relation to social behaviour. Edinburgh.